104

GABRIEL and the CREATURES

GABRIEL
and the
CREATURES

BY GERALD HEARD

Illustrated by Susanne Suba

HARPER & BROTHERS

PUBLISHERS ~ NEW YORK

To

Jay Michael Barrie

and

William Eliot Kiskadden

Contents

Preface

Evolution is the biggest story ever. The story of how Life has gone on climbing up through hundreds of millions of years and an amazing number of forms and shapes is the tale that out-sagas, out-epics, out-dramas every other saga, epic or drama. It is the all-over design in which every other event, adventure and discovery is merely a detail. It is not only so much the biggest of all the tales ever told, it is certainly no less the most wonderful. And, finally, it is so gripping because it is our tale. We human beings, we are its strange climax, its very latest chapter. One hundred and fifty years of world-wide study have been needed just to get the present outline. Still whole vast sections of the earlier parts are lacking. And how the parts we have found did actually fit onto each other —about that, too, there is still much discussion. But the nearer we come to the story's climax, the fuller and clearer it appears.

We human beings are mammals. That is an important link. It makes us akin with all those other animals who are so advanced that when they have their young the mother feeds the child with her own milk. The mammal age is the last stage of the Life Story. Certainly this invention of the family came after the Story of Life had closed a long and very complicated chapter—the vast period sometimes called the Middle Period of Life, the Mesozoic—the

age when the Lizards grew to vast size and into almost every possible shape. Then these giant lizards (Dinosaurs, etc.) died out.
The climate seems to have become unhealthy for them. The sea
spread widely, immense chalk-beds were laid down by the small
sea shells of innumerable little floating animals. But much more
important than that—on the land that remained there had appeared our small lively little ancestors. From that time (some sixty
million or more years ago) we have a wonderfully clear record. We
can find recordings in the rocks which show the mammals spreading everywhere. The mammal model is a sweeping success against
all the earlier forms of life. Nevertheless this first big burst of success made by these new competitors, doesn't (except in one case
and character) lead to further and final victory—quite the reverse.
Indeed a wise man has said, "Nothing fails like success." Certainly
all but one particular sort, or species, of mammal, has fallen into
the same kind of mistakes that seem to have destroyed their
predecessors, the Saurians.

The How They Did So, is fairly plain. But The Why They
Did So—about that there is far more debate and dispute. Few
people who have viewed the evidence doubt that at least all of us
mammals have come from a common type of ancestor. But quite
a number of experts still fail to agree why all animals, except man,
have now become so specialized that there seems very little hope
of their further advance, very little doubt that they are on the
way to extinction.

The stories that are given here are, then, attempting two things:
they try, first, to give in fairy-tale form, small sketches, illustrations, dramatizations out of the great saga of the mammals—our
story in its five great chapters—called by geologists the Eocene,
the Dawn of our age; the Oligocene when a few of our present
species had appeared; the Miocene; the Pliocene; and the Pleisto-
cene—when more and more of the present animals are known to

have arisen. But, secondly, these stories, because they are fairy stories, because the characters in them have wills and wishes, tastes and passions—as well as magic gifts and wizard powers—these characters choose and struggle and get enchanted by using their magic wrong and find deliverance by using it right. Is that—at least in parable form—the truth about Life, the meaning of the mammals' evolution, the reason why our ancestors struggled, the explanation why so many failed, and one stock—our own—is still struggling, struggling to become stronger, wiser, more aware? No one can be sure; perhaps no one ever will be. But it is the truth about ourselves—that we have to struggle and choose and deny our greed, our fear and our wish to slack; we have to keep going our interest, our wonder, our will to understand and to co-operate. So we may ask: What is so deeply true of us, may it not be bred in us, be an essential part of our nature we inherited from our ancestors and so, may be, in some way part of their experience? In the stories of the other animals choosing to be big, brutal, over-armed, and of the one that throughout clings to sensitiveness and general interest, curiosity and wonder (until this, the weak but aware, becomes man the master of all beasts) in this narrative we can at least see a myth of our present crisis, of our pressing choice and our unique opportunity.

Part I

THE FIRST-CHOICERS

A Prologue

The Group was very small—in both ways. It was very small in numbers—hardly half-a-dozen. And very small in size—not one of the six was more than six inches high, and none of them stood up properly—I mean they sat up and begged and then fumbled on their fore-paws. You'd have thought they were Lizards that hadn't yet learned how to lizard very well—and you'd have been right. And you'd have seen what very small fry they really were when you glanced from their little huddle, looking over their little flat heads and beady eyes, at their place of meeting—a spit of mud over which bent a broken-down tangle of creeper, and round which washed a greasy swill. The Group was on the edge of a huge

swamp filled with dreary dilapidated attempts at trees, with never a flower on them, and indeed not a proper leaf. That was dismal enough. But to the dismal was added the dangerous. For awash in the swamp, floundering in among the sticky herbage, were things as big as the trees, but tearing at them and gulping down fronds and roots, and bits of each other, and bellowing and snapping and writhing—the Dinosaurs, of course, going up to twenty tons, living to ten times twenty years and able, with a swing of paw or tail, to burst an elephant, as you'd burst a feather pillow.

But, though small, the Group was united. They had met to pass a resolution, complete with chairman and audience of five.

"We are met," the chairman piped in something less than a mouse's squeak, "to ask for co-operation. We are ready to advance. But we don't know what to do. We believe that we have been made ready for some new progress—but whither and how? We are undoubtedly creatures of promise. But, we ask, what has been promised us? And we ask further Who has given the promise?"

These telling questions were met by a burst of applause almost as loud as the croaking of some nearby frogs. A member supported the motion.

"I would only add," he said, "that what we have just heard is confirmed to my mind by what I can only call an air of expectancy. Indeed I would go further and suggest, perhaps it is this air that has inspired our appeal!"

This remark itself was apparently inspiring to the entire audience. They all began to look up. And, sure enough, the air itself did seem to be clearing. The dense brooding mist, with its almost suffocating warmth—like the hottest of hothouses—and its very distinct flavor, as though gas were leaking somewhere, fumy and fuggy, was lifting. Not only was the air you breathed fresher to nose and mouth—it was getting clearer to the sight. It turned from dingy gray to pearly gray and then began to tinge into blue, and the blue to harden from woolly blue to china blue. And that this was no private impression, the little audience on the mudbank soon saw. For already several of the great hulks of the saurians, out in the misty swamp, began to raise great blinking eyes on the end of stalk-like necks.

Never before had they been known to pay any attention to anything except the tepid smelly vegetable soup in which they floated and gulped, unless of course one of them stepped on another's face when the face was flattened by the foot or the foot swallowed by the face. But now after opening their eyes as wide as they would go, they opened their mouths as wide as well and reared up their snouts as far as they could reach. They were actually panting. They would have blustered with protest—had they known how. As it was they broke into a chorus of gasps, grunts, wheezes and coughs.

"I believe," squeaked the promising Lizard chairman, "I believe the curtain is rising. We are about to be called onto the stage."

The mist cleared even more. A whole vault of sky appeared. For a moment it seemed that there would be left an entire heaven of clean blue. And then, down across it ran an iridescent curve, a sweeping arch of light, a flying buttress launched from the zenith to the ground. The bridge was made of five layers of concentric colors. It grew as clear as a cascade, as definite as a roadway. And along its back swept a star of complete brightness—utterly shining white. As the star touched the earth the rainbow vanished. And in front of the somewhat startled congregation of Protomammals stood Gabriel, the Archangel, who for short is called Iris in Greek.

"Yes?" he asked in a voice very like C Major. The interrogated were taken aback. The chairman, however, managed to reply.

"We were wondering . . . ?"

"That is known. And, also, that you have a wish."

"Well, we have a suggestion . . ."

"I have said, You have a wish; your wish is granted. Now ask it!"

"Well, we thought . . . I mean. . . ."

"Your thoughts are known, of course. All you have to do—all we are waiting for, is for you to wish."

"Well, you know, we rather wanted—well, something to happen. I mean we felt that somehow we had been made ready for something. And we thought, I mean we rather wanted it—whatever it may be—to happen!"

"All right! Wish, then! That's all. That's everything. That's all you have to do. That's all you can do."

And then the great organ of a voice modulated into great gentleness. "But please don't think I'm patronizing you. Believe me, what I've asked you to do is more, far more than I could ever! I can be everywhere, see everything, report, present, render and express everything," the voice rose again and climbed and spread to a thunder of sound, till the whole sky rang as this greatest of all created creatures flung back his head. "I can, praise be to His Perfection, praise everything that He has made almost as it deserves to be praised!" And at that he opened his great mouth and there came from it a peal of delight that made the earth heave like a breaking billow, the whole air wave like a flag of triumph and the sky ring like a belabored gong. He shook his vast golden head, and as archangels have for hair flame, a blazing tide poured over his shoulders crackling like a newly stirred Christmas bonfire.

Then free of his monster laugh of joy, he called, "But I cannot wish! How could I, who see so much and see it all excellent. So wish well, oh seeds of inconceivable creation. Will, and it shall be wrought for you, by you and in you."

"Well, we wanted, you know, to begin . . . We felt ready to try—well, to do something, to be something that has never been before! We want, we wish, we WILL that The Will be done in us as it is done where you come from!"

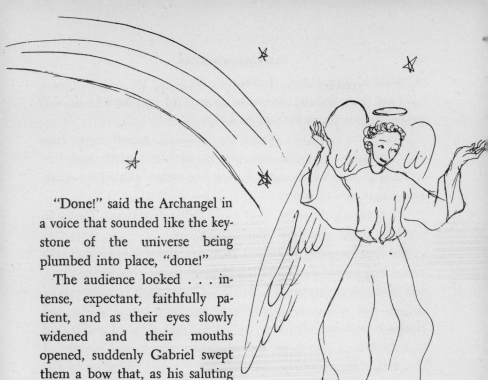

"Done!" said the Archangel in a voice that sounded like the keystone of the universe being plumbed into place, "done!"

The audience looked . . . intense, expectant, faithfully patient, and as their eyes slowly widened and their mouths opened, suddenly Gabriel swept them a bow that, as his saluting hand brushed close to the earth, left a weal of crocuses as a glowing trace.

"He who knows before told, grants before asked. He has prepared and now sends you the gifts which He knew you would request—the robe and the carpet. The robe you shall wear and the carpet you shall pass over as you enter on your way toward where His Will is no longer what shall be done, but is always and ever. Here, then, are the two gifts."

And putting his two hands behind his two ears he then swept forward, right down and under the beady eyes and twitching noses of his audience, both pairs of thumbs and fingers.

The audience goggled and sniffed to catch the first trace of the wonderful gifts prepared by the supremely creative, utterly wise Good-Will. They peered at the offering fingers, sniffed and then peered up at the huge smiling face that filled their sky.

"You are puzzled?" he asked, laughing. "So much divine

thought, so patient and vast a preparation! And the pretty pageant, timed so appositely to flash down across the cleared heaven. And a messenger so delighted with the fitness and abundance of the message, the grant, the endowment, the opportunity . . . And then this. Or, for it only makes it odder, these!"

"Well," said the chairman, "you see we don't quite see, I mean, how what we wished is so expressed by the Divine Will?"

"True enough, true enough. For you, feeling yourselves to be such small fry, among so much run-to-seed size, you think His gifts should be, must be, big to make you big. For, of course, you naturally think He must be big, and if you are to be like Him you must be bustingly big. But He is so awfully, terribly great because He is always and ever beyond all size—spaceless and timeless. We, His messengers and instruments, we are vast, and

swift as we are vast. But He, having no limit, has no definition. So He is not large any more than He is little. So, often the smallest cub, provided that it has never thought that it could ever be big and pushing, comes nearer to the core of Him, is held closer to that center which is really everywhere, than we can ever get."

"But," said the chairman, in a kind of expostulating apology, "all that, I'm sure, is very nice to know. But please—what actually have you, here in your two thumbs and fingers?"

The Archangel put his right hand under the chairman's nose, raised his first finger, and there on the ball of his glowing pink thumb lay a tiny streak of green, bright green at the tip and green-white at the bulbous other end.

"A very small leaf?" questioned the chairman. "Yes, their flavor is good when they're as small as that. But you have to pick them larger if you're to have a meal."

"No," said the Archangel. "No, it isn't a leaf. It's a new thing. It is going to carpet the whole world. Those great swamps are going to be dried out. They will become vast plains and they will be covered. They won't stay great dust flats. They will be carpeted, tapestried with a beautiful waving mantle of green. And the green shall grow further a lovely fringe. And that fringe will be gold and heavy with golden beads. And those beads will be your new food, Bread. The grass shall be your carpet, and your tablecloth and the bread upon your table."

And he waved his hand: the jungle vanished, the stagnant swamps were dried. As for the Dinosaurs, they had become simply lime to enrich the earth. So on the great brown areas there came a faint flush of green. And it grew thicker and waved in the wind. It grew darker and became tawny in the sunlight. It stood up supple and strong; thick, inexhaustible fields of rye and barley and millet and wheat.

And then he shook open his left hand, bringing back the attention of the audience to his second close-up. And on the ball of his left thumb there was lying also a faint streak, but even thinner and duller than the first shoot of grass. It was brown and very thin and the little bulb at the end, its root, was even smaller.

"Forgive me," said the chairman of the Sub-Lizards, "but your gifts get smaller, don't they?"

"And therefore always of more power, more potentiality," smiled back the conjuror Cherub, "and this, as it is more powerful than grass, is for yourselves. The grass was to clothe the earth. This is to clothe you."

The audience gazed at one another. "After all," said one to the other, "don't you think we look all right as we are? Perhaps we might be bigger. But I must say that a neat coat of iridescent

scales, or dull-polished shagreen, has always seemed to me in the best taste and very attractive."

Then, turning to the Archangel, "Do you mean that we are to shed our costumes and come out all covered over with threads like that? I don't think it would suit us, from the point of view of looks, and besides, surely it would be terribly inconvenient. Think of the difficulty of keeping it clean, and it would wear out so soon and it would give no proper protection—how could it?"

"Just try."

The chairman felt that the remark was aimed at him. He had called the meeting, and had evidently, if inadvertently, called down on their heads this instant answer to their demand. So he stood forward awkwardly, in the way that most people stand when their tailors say they have to be "tried on." And the Archangel, like the tailor, swept his hand down the customer's figure. The scales rippled off, as leaves come sweeping down from a tree in an autumn gale. But as they shed, in their place spread and sprouted a lovely glossy fur. As the Archangel's hand touched the small creature's heel, it stood complete in its new coat, as supple and fresh as an amber stream. All the others exclaimed, "My! But that's becoming!"

"It is," said the Archangel, "but all becoming, though it's the only way to being, takes time." Then turning to the new fashion he asked, "How does it feel?"

"Why, it's wonderful," said the transformed chairman, "one feels as though clothed in air, it's so light. And yet it's warm, too!"

The Archangel suddenly puffed out his cheeks and from his lips came a whistle of air so cold that as it shot down on the chairman it precipitated snow. And immediately everyone laughed, for, with a shudder, he'd suddenly become twice his size. All his hair

was standing on end and so his coat was twice as thick, but he
laughed back, though shivering a little. Then the Archangel
opened his mouth wider and the snowy blast hit the whole group,
and the rest just wilted over and lay hibernating, quite limp and
helpless like wax candles in weather that's too hot for them. With
another breath—this time a warm one—he brought the five back
to life and this time he and the chairman shared the laugh at the
other's expense. Then while the chairman had turned round to
tell the revived and won-over rest how wonderful it was to have
fur instead of scales—and so had his back for a moment to
Gabriel—the Archangel with the tip of his finger touched the
topmost floss that like a fine silver shadow crested the chairman's
ear. Immediately the touched one turned.

"You see," laughed the Gift-Bringer, "each of these hairs,
though it protects you so well from cold—as scales never could—
can signal right into you at the finest touch. Though you have
a far better blanket than ever a scale coat could be, you have also
a wonderful touch-telephone system, every hair signaling, right
below your skin to tell you what you are up against. Those hand-
some silky whiskers and eyebrows, those fine tips to ears and
tail"—and he gently touched each amber plume—"each of these
will let you walk through the dark and tell you when you are in
touch with things before you run into them."

"What an ingeniously clever gift, how simple, what fun!" they
called, all five. "Give us all fur coats!"

"You have them," shouted the Archangel. They looked about
them. But even the chairman's was gone; he was all scaly again
like the rest of them. "And the wonderful wheat fields—each
with that condensed food-packet in every one of those golden
ears of grain?" they cried as they looked about them. For already
the rolling lawns and vast savannas of harvest had vanished. Only
the old immovable swamp spread round them. "What do you
mean!" they cried in dismay.

"I mean," said the messenger—and already the great rainbow bridge was cresting down to fetch him home—"I mean that already it is all promised surely to you. Already the gift to grow the wonderful crop called hair is in you and with that will come to you warm blood and constant consciousness. You shall be more alive, more awake than any other creature has ever been so far. And as you grow thus, within and without, so too the grass which I have now sown, will step by step keep pace with your growth and pave and carpet the path along which you will advance."

The rainbow was now at the Archangel's heels. As he made a beautiful backward dive up its gleaming cataract, they heard his voice like a modulating chord, "Only keep small, keep flexible, keep sensitive, keep wondering, keep guessing, right up to the top of your highest hope and a little beyond, and if you will keep on making still one more daring guess, then your guess will become true beyond anything that has ever been, beyond anything that you could have ever guessed."

And he was gone, and the rainbow after him; and the sky began to mist over again and the grunts of the Dinosaurs filled the air. But the chairman concluded the meeting in a voice that was full of hope, "I guess brothers, that's just what we have to do."

And the unanimous motion ran, "We guess we will."

STORIES OF THE ANIMALS
WHO GOT THEIR WISHES

The Sea-Loungers

Everyone was still on the shore. Now, however, it was more or less a proper shore: not merely a mud bank in a swamp, as before. There was a real beach with waves, on the one hand, and grass coming down to the sand, on the other. There were plenty of rock-pools in between. And above that a clear enough sky. You could see at a glance, things had been cleaned up quite a lot. As sailors say, they were more or less shipshape. Everyone, too, was in pretty good form. They were a tidier, more able-bodied crew than had met to decide on fur for scales and grass instead of gum trees. However, they still seemed more than a little uncertain. They looked like nimblish sort of monster mice, but not as lithe as a really good rat at his best.

And this certain kind of vagueness of carriage and cut was expressed in their behavior. They milled about a bit—then one scratched an ear, another investigated his tail, a third tried to do a little rather scatter-brained grooming. Some glanced up at the grass banks above them; others scrabbled among the seaweed and some looked again and again out to sea.

Finally, one of the group spoke up for them, "Look here!" He sounded almost a little defiant. At the tone the others did look, a little startled. "Look here! You know, I don't really think much of this new life, after all. Tell the truth, I'm rather tired of all this grass-and-grain-gathering and scurrying about. Where's it getting us, anyhow? It's surely fatiguing. Life was much easier before, wasn't it? Just fishing out the soft roots and fronds that were awash in the water, paddling in the warm mud, taking naps in the trees and sleeping right through all the cold weather."

At that moment a fish swam effortlessly up to the surface of one of the larger pools near which they were all sitting. The fish blew a bubble, swallowed a large fly and with a wave of his tail cruised off into the sea-fronds, where it floated in dozing ease.

"There, that's the life! No exertion; food everywhere, rest anywhere. Bed and board always at hand. Just wish to be anywhere, and with a swish, hardly knowing, you glide along. Your dinner slips into your mouth, instead of your having to pick and glean and garner!"

The group was attending. The speaker became emphatic. "I ask—are we certain that we took the right turning when we came out of the swamp? I'm not! 'Deed the more I think of it the more I'm sure we didn't!"

"Well, we couldn't have stayed there?" someone half-questioned. "The scene was shifted, as you might say. We had to move on?"

"Yes, yes," the first speaker interrupted, "but we were free to move and I want to propose that we moved in the wrong direction, and I want to second my proposal by moving that we remove, and now, in what I'm now sure is the right one."

"You don't mean," said the same half-questioner, "you don't mean that we could very well go anywhere else now? I mean, now it's a matter of Land or Sea. And surely we've plumped for the land? You know, even if we'd really like to, we just can't be fishes! We can't, just by wishing, just get back and live in the water!"

"Why not?" Everybody wheeled round. It wasn't the first

speaker's voice. It wasn't the voice of any of this little shore-crew.
And yet it wasn't unfamiliar to any of them. For, of course, it
was Iris Gabriel who had turned up. In this clearer, colder air he
looked rather more like molten gold than iridescent mother-of-
pearl. He hadn't slid down a rainbow this time. He'd flashed out,
as the sun will fire a sunbeam from over the rim of a black cloud
and plunge it into a lake.

"Why not?" he repeated, and certainly at that tone no one
could imagine why one shouldn't do anything one wished. There
seemed to be all the liberty of all the world in the very sound.
"Do you really want to go back, back, right back; behind the
Saurians and their shallow lagoons, back right under the deep,
deep sea? You really wish to go into reverse?"

His voice wasn't threatening, scolding, hectoring. But it was,
of course, immensely loud, and, as he rolled out the sentence,
everything seemed to vibrate, quiver, tremble, till you really felt
that the vast, oh-so-slow-moving, wheels of Time had been suddenly put into a rushing racing reverse and were re-rolling, re-
winding the heaped-up web of things, back to the primal sea level,
back till the land sank out of sight and everything was awash.

The audience was certainly shaken out of any conviction that
nothing much more could happen to them—that they had arrived
at any settled and final state. Even the reactionary who had moved
and seconded the meeting into its present pass and partial protest—even he seemed for a moment a little taken aback. Still,
when he faced up to the great Archangel, that vast column of
light, standing between earth and heaven, didn't look like an
angry exclamation mark. In fact, the immense figure actually began
to bend, and so gracefully, yes, so humbly that at last he looked
more like a great question mark than anything else. You felt he
was actually asking for your views—and certainly the first speaker
had his!

"I want. . . ."

"Yes," said the Archangel, in a voice like the wind when it brings a lake alive, or makes a forest unfurl all its new leaves. You were sure something already had been recorded. For of course, Gabriel is the one who writes into fact what we can only put into words. That's why at the End, His Master and ours will say to him, "Gabriel, my Secretary-Son, would you now please read us the Minutes of the last meeting of the Solar System."

"Yes," came that wonderful sound of all possible assent and good will. "Yes," and at this third yes—just as when the auctioneer says GOING GOING GONE!—the first speaker now felt certain, absolutely certain that he knew what he wanted and that he was out for it.

"I've said, I see no reason for supposing this land life, with all its scurrying and struggling and chewing and chilling, is really in the right direction. You say," and he cocked a challenging eye at the stooping Arc of light, "you say, all of our wishes aren't used up? Do I take you rightly?" The angelic Arc bent even lower in assent, till he arched right over the little crowd (as a great fountain may bend under a gale). "I take"—and there was growing assurance, indeed assertion, in the tone and attitude the speaker took—"I take silence for consent! Very well, then, I have made up my mind. I want to go back into the sea. Look, I haven't forgotten how to swim!" He dived into the pool nearby, and certainly, made some quite respectable going.

"He'll tire of it soon?" said someone dubiously.

"Not if he doesn't wish to," remarked the Archangel.

"It's fine in here," shouted the rat who was resolved they should pool their resources.

"But he can't become a fish!" another protested.

"No, but he can sell his gift and buy with it almost all the things which the fishes had given them." The voice spoke in the quiet tone of a careful accountant checking over still liquid assets. Then, modulating a little, into that of a wise banker consulting with a rich but really very stupid depositor, he called down to the swimmer, "You really want to sell your holding of the land and to make this repurchase of the sea?"

"You bet!" said the swimmer over his shoulder. "This is the life!"

"Well," said the vast angelic voice, "mind, this is for life!" And for the first time there was something almost like a sigh in the sentence. Anyhow at that sound a big swell that had been rolling off the foreshore began to rise, swept up like the shoulder of a hill and flooded into the pool making it part of the sea. Those still on the rock scampered up to safety on the grass-crowned cliff. The swimmer was caught and swept away out into the ocean. "Now watch," said the Archangel. And as archangels aren't allowed (and don't want) to tell you to do things you can't, he lent to the little crowd his own sea-and-land scanning sight. He did this by throwing the great prism of his rainbow like a giant magnifying lens or eye before their little beady ones. So they saw they could follow quite well their adventurous fellow as he made his way out over the waste of waters. "Now watch," said the Archangel again, "watch him spend his incomparable birthright. Look at his feet!" And sure enough he was now swimming so well, giving his whole heart and mind to it, that his feet were turning more and more into a kind of two-bladed rudder, a tail. They couldn't turn into an up-and-down tail as proper fishes have. They still had to stick out more or less right and left as all proper feet, all our feet do, especially when we go swimming. But if you insist on selling your feet for a fin-tail, well, it was a fair enough answer to such a profoundly silly demand.

"You see, it isn't real creation," whispered the Archangel to his little brood, above which he was hovering like an immense bird.

"It's sham, really. The poor fellow has been let put the process into reverse. But he can't really even recreate. He Who Never Forgets, never permits any of His creation wholly to obliterate what with His first creative word He wrote in their hearts and gave them as their endowment, the word of everlasting freedom."

"Oh look!" cried one of the brood. "His arms are going, and now his hands and fingers."

"Yes, you see he had to change them into side-fins instead."

"Why, he couldn't get his hands to his mouth now!"

The squeak of protest carried across the water and their transformed associate turned round as he swam. He turned his whole vast body, slowly in a great gradual sweep, as a ship has to turn, till he was facing them.

"Can't you turn your head?" someone called.

"What's the need—it's easier to roll round if you're floating."

"He can't," whispered Gabriel. "His neck now is stiff and solid as a pole. For so long he's had no interest in anything but food-shoveling that all the upper vertebrae of his spine have now fused, have stuck together into one inflexible bone."[1]

"But your hands!" they called again. "Surely you want them!"

"What's the use! No need to pick, fiddle and choose if all you have to do is just open your mouth and get your fill! Look!"

And sure enough, his great mouth was full of fishes. For, though he had grown vastly, yet he had proved right in one way. He wanted easy feeding and fish by schools were being swept into his yawning throat.

"You'll choke and drown," they cried.

"Not I!" he shouted and dived.

"One, two, three," they went on counting till they were tired and waiting till they were all of a fuss—for they weren't very good at reckoning or at keeping on just watching. But he was certainly gone a long while. Finally they turned to Gabriel in dismay.

But all he said was "Wait!"

They waited again, turned again and waited still again. Gabriel had to give them ever so many shots of his own eternal patience, or they would never have sat it out. But, finally, there was a sudden upheaval in the sea, a great spout of water and there was their super-sea-changed friend frolicking about.

"Pouff!" he said, blowing a plume of spray thirty feet into the air. "It's fine, fifty fathoms down! And the fishing, Oh Boy!"

"He's boasting, isn't he?" they said, turning timorously to their heavenly friend.

"No," he told them.

"How do you do it?" they called out to the swimmer.

"Oh I don't know," he answered carelessly, "it's really quite easy, you know. At least it is for me. I just wish and it works!"

"That's just half the truth," the Archangel murmured. And then loud enough for the Sea-Lounger to hear . . . "If you've been to fifty fathoms why don't you get 'the bends' when you come back? The bends," he added in a whisper to the group, "is a horrid thing that gets you if you come up too quickly when you've dived too deep."[2]

"Oh, I suppose I know the trick," came the jaunty answer.

"He doesn't," whispered the Archangel. "He doesn't know what he's doing. He's using up all the inventive power, all the choice-energy, all the wish-force that was in him—and is still unspent in you. But it's true, the inventive power in him was so great, it's not only made him unwieldly big—when he let its unseen force escape and take form and shape—it has actually got him round the bends. Yes, the amount of invention that's locked up in your little bodies still makes me marvel." The AA's ruminative whisper was drowned as the great sham-fish smacked his false tail with a bang on the sea.

"This is the life for an inventive guy," he roared and spouted another jet of water out of his nose in breezy contempt for the timid little crew on the shore. The puff was as fine as steam. In fact it was his hot lung breath condensing in the cold air, as ours does when the weather is frosty. But it looked ridiculously like that whiff of a cigar which a big, boasting executive sometimes will give after having told the press what a top-notch tycoon he really is. "Look what lounging's done for me," he spouted on. "Look how I've grown. I'm never coming back, you bet. You'd all better come out here."

"You'll chill to death," they twittered, shivering a bit themselves.

"Gosh! haven't you yet tumbled to my cuteness!" He chuckled again. "I'm warmer than ever we were on that drafty land. I've grown my own insulation! Look at me!" He did look like someone wrapped up in a big black rubber swimming suit—a great overblown bolster. "That's my fat—comes from proper living, living a perfectly balanced life. Didn't I know this is the right life—the way life should be lived—right because it's easy! Didn't I say I'd beat the fishes? Any fool can have the land for all I care. I've got the sea. Don't be little sand-shore sissies. Come along in. Come to sea and see the real world from the right angle!"

Several of the trial rats turned to Gabriel questioningly.

"Yes, you can go too if you wish." His voice was as level as the sea horizon; so you couldn't guess whether he wished you to go or stay.

"But we couldn't change like that?" said a couple timorously.

"Do you wish to?"

"Well, we didn't ask that. We asked could we ever grow as he's grown—strong and big and full of built-in gadgets?"

"But you're really asking. Should you wish to? You really admire him, don't you?"

"Well, you see we are rather mingy and we do have to work pretty hard to get our fare and the weather's often wet and the grain poor and our burrows damp. Please, we're not complaining really. But he does seem, doesn't he, to have bettered himself?"

"You think so?"

"Please," said one of the group, who was already making for the shore, "please tell me this, distinctly," and his little voice was crisp. "I do understand you, don't I, that if I really wish to go and live that easy sensible life and leave this rather, rather dubious . . ."

"Precarious, I should put it," interpolated the AA.

"Why precarious?" whispered someone.

"Because," whispered back the Archangel, "*precarious* he thinks, means even more dubious than doubtful, and it actually means what I mean, something that needs praying about!"

"Well," continued the seceder No. 2, "in this rather precarious life, then I might succeed as well as he has?"

"Quite, quite," said the AA. And at each "quite," the new deserter took a hop, and there he was in the pool.

And for him, too, the big swell rose, came and took him, and he went out riding and chortling over and through the waves.

But when the first sea-escapist saw the second coming after, he wasn't really pleased. "All this overcrowding!" he gurgled-grumbled to himself. "Won't be a fish left soon, at this pace! Well, I must think up a few more of my brilliant body-miracles." So he pushed out farther from their native shores. He found seas—the farther toward the ice he went—that were just a-scum with shrimp and such like small sea food. But of course it was colder, so he grew still bigger and laid on still more fat till he was feet thick in blubber. The Archangel on his side made his iris-lens still stronger so the little group lingering on the land could continue to follow the escapists. The second one was now where the first had been, and he had grown as big. The first, however, the farther away he had gone, the bigger he had grown.

"He's now bigger than any of the Saurians you used to fear," the great Recording Angel noted, "none of them ever managed to grow to that size. He's the biggest-ever of all animals." It was true though scarcely believable. He would grow until he was a hundred feet long. Of course to be that length he had to be lying down all the time. For no inventive wish-power in the whole world could make a flesh-and-blood giant one hundred feet high. He'd break down at the feet and indeed all over. No, this giant just had to be floated. For he weighed one hundred twenty tons.

"And he was once as small as us!" The group gasped with a mixture of admiration and puzzlement.

"That shows how much is still in you, if you will—but not to have your wish," said the great voice in the sky above them.

"We don't quite understand," the audience remarked. And it was clear they weren't even wanting to, very much. They were engrossed in watching their transformed companion. He certainly had grown prodigiously. But what was even odder than his blowing up to this unbelievable size, was the way he had shaped himself, the design he was evidently working out. He was, it was clear, determined to beat all the fishes at their own game and on their own ground (or rather in their own element) he, a creature that still had to breathe! And he had gone quite a long way to beating them.

For instance, all fishes have big mouths, partly because they have no hands. He had grown a mouth that surpassed any of theirs. His mouth had grown faster, much faster than the rest of him. He was far the biggest of all animals but far more odd; no animal in all the world had ever grown such a monster mouth, such jaws so grotesquely outsize. His head was now more than one-third of his whole length and the great hollow of his mouth itself was bigger than all the room taken up by his lungs and stomach. Obviously, he had sacrificed everything to make himself into nothing but a monster food-scoop. His lips were so wide that he really had nothing else in his face. Even his eyes had slid down till they were tucked away like dimples or pimples in the pucker of those absurd lips. His ear, even smaller, was a tinier hole behind his tiny eye. And even then, it was more for looks than for use. For if you spend so much of your life diving, your ears are bound to protest. They are made to give you information by their responding to the changing pressure, the ebb and flow of very small airwaves, sound waves. If you keep on plunging and plugging them with dense-pressure water, they must burst, give you no further service and no end of trouble. So the whales have used part of their inventive power just to destroy one of the greatest of the gifts which all of us creatures have been given. They have used their power of growth to ungrow their ears by growing flesh to block them. The big Arctic Whale still has an ear track. But the next candidate for fish-form, for whalehood, the one which we'll see in a moment was even fonder of deep diving, he's closed his ears for good. Now that alone, it's obvious, is a very dangerous step. We often say of a stubborn fool heading for a fall, "He won't listen to anyone!" But, as a matter of fact, though we can shut our eyes by dropping our lids, we can't close our ears, save for a moment and not very effectively with our fingers. Our eyes close in sleep, not our ears. They are our sleepless sentinels all through the dark. Just this fact, then, that the whales grew flesh to block their ears shows how all their daring diving was in point of fact only making a header toward extinction.[3] Practically blind, all but stone deaf (it is just possible he can hear a little through vibrations piercing through his block of a head)—look at him wallowing. An animated, overgrown spoon, shoveling itself through an ocean of gravy.

His former companions couldn't take their eyes off him as he bulldozed along through the waves. And he was still able (probably owing to Gabriel) to call back to them—though there was now something a little frothy about his enunciation. "One more of my bright ideas," he shouted, opening his mouth so wide they thought he must have split and they'd fall into the big black cavity. "See," he gurgled. "No teeth now. Damned nuisance, teeth. Damn bore chewing. Look!" And he waved great fringe-curtains of whalebone from under his lips. "Just cruise ahead all day and drink as you drive, 'live on soup and live in it'—that's my motto." And they saw him wallow along, just gulping in by the million tiny sea-creatures, filtering them through his whale-bone fringes and swallowing them all the while. "Feeding's as easy and as regular as breathing," he gurgled again, "just as it ought to be. 'Eat as you breathe'—that's another of my mottoes. Look at the size it's made me. One whisk of my tail and I could bang the whole brood of you into a batter. Your feathered friend no doubt thinks I've gone soft and water-logged. Well, let me tell you that of the ten parts of me four are pure muscle. So I generate more than five hundred times more energy than the strongest of you ever will unless you're sensible and come back into the sea. Look, I just gallop through the waves!"

He certainly was rushing ahead like a pretty fast ship, in fact at twenty knots. His boast was quite true, he was generating some five hundred twenty horsepower.[4]

The Group glanced up again at Gabriel. "It's true," he said, slowly smiling. "I know it sounds like a joke and I know it amazes even me, but it's a fact and you must face it."

"But going that speed," squeaked someone, using Gabriel as their radio to their bloated fellow who had made himself into a submarine, "going that speed, and with your eye bogged in your mouth's dimple, you'll run into something, rushing headlong, running blind! A rock or a chunk of sharp-edged ice, you'll run full tilt into it and with your weight!"

"Do you suppose that matters to me?" puffed back the cruiser.

"Didn't I tell you that nearly half of me is pure muscle? I'm the toughest thing ever. If I ran into anything, why I'd just bounce off. The strongest blow, the sharpest point, just glances off my head. So head-along I go—and let the others look out when we meet head on!"[5]

"But you might run into enemies?"

"Me, ME, MEE!!! Why, I'd just shoulder them aside. Look at my size—who could take a bite at me! Besides, haven't I told you, I'm tough, tougher than the hardest, toughest root, I'm tough all over. Nothing has ever been harder chewing than me! See, I'm the greatest piece of muscle that ever spanked the sea, tidal-waved the land and washed down the sky. Why, I could clean the clouds and shampoo half the seraphs with the splash I can make!"

Some of the group tittered; all were obviously impressed. A few looked round and up a trifle nervously to see how Gabriel was taking it. But all he said was, "Keep on looking." The huge Polar Whale (for that of course was what he had become) paraded up and down, sweeping sea-soup into his huge drolling mouth, and every now and then giving another ear-splitting slap with his tail on the sea.

But after a little, things didn't seem going quite so well. He looked as though he had something in his mouth that didn't taste so good. In fact he began to spit and foam. But of course, table manners for him had long gone overboard. And this foam had something not at all nice about it. It was a suspicious sort of red. The big boastful monster was bleeding at the mouth.

"He can't have bitten his tongue," remarked one of the on-lookers, "he hasn't any teeth—one of his boasted advances on us."

"But something is biting him," replied Gabriel. And the Arch-angel suddenly enlarged the magnification which he was lending his brood, still further. At that moment the poor boaster threw open his huge jaws. The audience felt they were looking into a sea-cavern through which the tide was racing and in that tide were swift cruel-looking swimmers, who were tearing with rows of skewer teeth at a big tortured animal whose blood made the sea-water crimson.

"That writhing, helpless member is your poor overblown companion's tongue! True, he can't bite it. Doesn't he wish he could. Then he'd snap and swallow up these pirates that are eating out his mouth. It's a pretty mess, isn't it? You see two can play at that game of the muscular gorger. Those smaller gorgers are even tougher than he; they can swim even faster and they're cute enough to have learned one thing about toughness that he overlooked. You can be tough up to a point, you can be tough all over outside, you can put your eye—that has to be soft—into a pocket, and your ear—that someone might pull—you can pull it down under your leather hide and you can make your nose like a battering ram. But if you are to eat you must be soft. There's no way of making muscle save by taking in food and making it soft enough for your soft insides to take it in. Otherwise you starve and all your boasted muscle just vanishes. No, he let his teeth go. But he couldn't, daren't let his tongue follow. His tongue remained and in order that it might do the work of keeping him going it remained ·soft. So it is there that these tougher guys have found out where they can get him."

"But can't he swallow them whole and just digest them, suffocate them, acid-bath them? He's big enough to do that, even if he can't bite them up?" someone excitedly asked. "Look," and their eyes were directed down the cavernous mouth right to the back. It narrowed and narrowed till you couldn't see there was a throat.

"Oh yes," Gabriel answered. "Yes, he can swallow, just. But you see, when he made his seemingly brilliant labor-saving discovery of living on nothing but sea-soup, what was the use of a throat which could have swallowed a shark whole? No doubt his digestion had an easier, slacker time on soup, pure and simple. And his throat also saw no reason why it should remain any longer unnecessarily open. So his closing mind let that close too. As for his hands, for which he found no use but to turn them into paddles to push him through the soup—you see, literally, he can't raise a finger to flick one of these cruel, skewering snappers out of his mouth."

The audience recoiled and Gabriel in obedience to their obvious wish to withdraw, put the picture again into long distance.

"I rather feel," remarked someone after a pause, while the large shuddering hulk slowly drifted out of view, "indeed it's clear—obviously he made a mistake."

"Yes, yes," remarked another. "But he obviously thought up, at first, some very cute notions. I'd no idea, I must confess, that we had so much inventive capacity in us."

"He went too far, without a doubt," this was from a third member of the Group, "but look there!"

In the middle-distance had appeared some warm-water Whales, a school of Dolphins, curvetting as prettily as you could wish, and another school of Porpoises which were diving and snapping up fish and doing so with teeth that even a Shark might envy—or at least respect. And one of the whales (he's called now a Sperm Whale) at that moment dived. He was down quite a bit but when he came up he had more than a mouthful. Indeed, all round his head was laced and strapped a writhing gray mass of tentacles, while a monstrous parrot beak strove to bite his head open. It was a battle royal and the little audience goggled with excitement. The giant Cuttlefish (for that's what it was) had evidently been torn from its sea-floor moorings and now was making a last desperate struggle to suffocate and drag down its enemy. The huge jaws of the Sperm Whale were, however, anything but toothless. Great

rows of ivory tusks clamped and chumped. The ten terrible
tentacles (for the Cuttlefish was the largest of all that tribe, the
monstrous decapod), the great boa constrictor arms, each of them
bossed their whole length with thorn-edged suction pads, that
could suck the flesh off our bodies, as you suck a rather rich ice
cream, these great armored coils fell off one by one, lopped, as
the gardener's shears lop off green-withies. The whale then gave
half-a-dozen great gulps—and dinner was over.

"That's surely the strenuous life!"

"No decadence there!"

"He's certainly a mighty fine he-man hunter." The little chorus
of excited, and perhaps almost a little defiant praise, rose from
round the Archangel's feet.

"Still, · you know," Gabriel remarked, "even he, the mighty
Sperm Whale, isn't really as strong as he looks. That poor even-
bigger brother that went up to the soupy seas of the poles, he had

still another weakness which the fighting whale shares with him. If you go back to be like a fish, well, you must share a fish's limitations. Some of the most serious don't show. But they're there *all* the time. Fish certainly aren't anything like as free to move, as you are—though it takes you more effort to do it. So all of you who go back into the sea must accept no end of invisible frontiers which you who stick to being crawlers and creepers can pass. For instance, water that seems just pleasantly warm to you may prove fatal to that big Arctic Whale. Often it will do for him—just as though he'd been boiled. While that fine husky-toothed fighter, if he gets into a bay and ice water should drift across the bay's mouth, he's imprisoned. It's death for him to get shut in more than a little while in water that is life to his big brother.[6] And, mind you, every one of those of you who go sea-native, every one will end as helpless as the first—" Gabriel paused, and then concluded, "One way or another."

"What d'you mean," suddenly whisked out one of the more attentive of the Group, "*one way or another?* There's only one way, isn't there, for those that go back? You just turn into a helpless soup-scoop, a giant sea-sucker?"

"Yes and no. In any case you do become a helpless sucker. But there's even an uglier way down into the abyss than becoming a shrimp addict."

At that moment more porpoises swam into view. As they came abreast they were obviously enjoying fine fishing. Then suddenly their ranks broke and one plunged off in desperate haste. But not fast enough. Darting after him appeared a creature like him but behaving like a shark. A moment more and the pursuer had its prey seized. With savage fury it tore the writhing body to pieces, swallowing whole hunks off the still living animal.

"What's this?" the Group squeaked in panic chorus.

"That," said Gabriel, "that is another short-cutter making for extinction. He's found that the easiest of all feeding is to feed off his fellows. He's the Killer Whale. It was him you saw, feasting off the tongue of his big helpless brother. Yet, he was once, like the others, one of you. Then he slunk back into the sea. And now he's thought up this cunning idea—how to go one better than the rest and exploit them for their mistake. They sponge away at the sea, turning its soup into their blood. Then he cuts in with his further labor-saving notion. He shortens the process even more by drinking not sea-soup but the blood of the soup drinkers. He's made them his stomach as it were. Sharp, isn't it! But wait a moment—maybe in the end it will prove as stupid a mistake as theirs."

At that moment a Killer Whale again came to the surface. But

this time he wasn't making trouble for others. He was evidently in it himself. He gasped and rolled and convulsed. "He's choking!" cried someone in a voice more excited than sympathetic. It was obviously true. The pirate gave one more convulsion-gasp. "He's choked!" cried the vocal onlooker. Again there was no denying it. The demonic creature lay floating on its back, as helpless as a baby, its cruel mouth agape and grinning like the hungry monster whales it so often gorged on. The dead animal was drifting near the shore. They could see the distended jaws stuffed by what looked like leather.[7]

"He's so overcharged with blood-lust," said Gabriel, "it has actually choked him. He's suffocated himself in his frenzy, literally, to get the other fellow down. He was too tough, too bolting savage, even to wait quietly to chew up his poor victims. In the end, when it came to a tug-of-war between their hides and his insides, their tough coats and his soft throat, they got their revenge simply because of his insane greediness."

The body floated away again. No one said anything more till the suicide carcass was out of sight. The sea-surface remained enigmatically unruffled, hiding its mysterious secrets and tragedies under a quicksilver calm. Finally, that one of the group who always seemed more interested in what Gabriel said about it than in the passing show itself, asked hesitatingly, "Do you think any more of us are going to slip back to sea?"

Gabriel looked down at the little crew. "I'm no foreteller. My job's to record. None of us angels are much good at foreseeing. The Prophets, you know, have a department of their own. Indeed, it's so big I might call it a Ministry—the Ministry of the Morrow. And they're recruited, I believe, from another species. But I do know this—if you lose patience with plodding and the hard dusty uphill way, you'll fall back into the sea. If you think size and an easy life is a short cut to comfort and security—well, there doesn't seem any way out from that mistake, you'll just find yourselves whaling away, till you're left stranded. I have a suspicion (mind you, I'm no prophet so your guess is as good as mine) but for what it's worth my hunch is that this kind of temptation to secede is going to haunt all of you for quite a while. I've a feeling you'll be let go back to the sea almost as often as you wish. We'll see, we'll see. The sea . . ." and he became reflective, almost talking to himself, looking out over its huge curved mirrors, "the sea is a sort of siren. It promises final rest, to float forever rocked to sleep, at last settled down from all striving, at sea level. But the sea at surface level has no rest. Only deep, deep down in the dark still cold is there final rest at primal sludge-level. Of course you can slide down till you can slide no more, if you wish. It's rest of a sort, but, I promise you, it isn't peace. And I am the Angel of Peace—not the Angle of Rest."

And on the punch of that pun, Gabriel shot up at an angle that was as beautiful, daring and unrestful as when a lightning flash springs out from the earth and stabs the sky.

The audience looked about it questioningly. "Well, I suppose we'd better just keep on waiting and trying," someone said at last rather ruminatively. "I guess," he added, "there may be more in the land than you'd think and perhaps more in us than we feel. But what?"

And still looking for that answer they ambled off.

The Mowing-Machines

Of course a lot of time had passed, and equally of course, the only time that mattered or will ever matter was that that made a difference. The time of our crew was marked in their growth. They shifted off the shore and they began really to face up to the land; the land that was what you might call park-land. They browsed a bit but nibbled more, liking the ends of shoots and the nuts that often tantalizingly dangled from the ends of fine branches, branches they were getting a bit too heavy to trust themselves on.

It was, then, quite early in what is called our (the mammal) Dawn Age, the Eocene, that one of us made another of those amazing mistakes, a whale of a mistake, but this time he made it on the land. It seems that he kept on reaching—his ideal was to be able to browse off the very tops of the trees, just to get the best of the curly bits and fruits right at the tip of his tongue. But he wouldn't look about him and see how he could get round and climb up and so get his hand on that piece of leaf or fruit that hung above him. He wouldn't even keep on stretching out his hand. No, he would only prance about keeping on greedily yearning, stretching, pushing out his mouth and neck and longing with every ounce of the fatal wish-power in him to be bigger and bigger—until it did turn literally into tons of bigness. Of course,

49

he couldn't become the size of a Whale. He had the sense to see
that he ought to stay on land. And that put whale-scale out of
the question. A whale can be a whale—we have seen—because he
can float himself. But this beast did pretty well in making a
monster fool of himself. He determined to be as big as the land
Dinosaur and, by horns and humps, he did. Yes, and he stood
taller than, as far as we know, any dinosaur ever succeeded in
rearing itself up on dry land. Of course, to get up to that size and

height, he had to make a number of cripplingly clever inventions. For he had nothing but bones, made of just the same lime as ours are made of, to hold him up. That always makes the problem of size a grave one for all of us. So, of course, he had to sacrifice his hand when he wanted to rear himself up—already he was far too heavy to stay on his hind legs.

We have this monster's bones now in New York at the American Museum of Natural History. They were found in the far west of India, Baluchistan. The bones at the end of his fore-limbs— what must have been his ancestors' fingers when they were small fry—are now almost fused together. They have to be; for with

them the fool made for himself a cluster-post, a muscle-bound faggot. And on this expensive improvised stilt, this super-cask of a creature evidently succeeded in waddling about. He stood seventeen feet at the shoulder and evidently at last won up to his ambition and could browse with his long muzzle—at the end of his flat head—off higher parts of the trees than anyone else could. In fact, he was so big that he was very soon done with. He appeared at that Dawn Age and in that Dawn Age he stumped through his whole history. He was gone before the sunrise of mammal life, before that first chapter of our history had been completed. He's been gone for far longer than the whole time he took to grow and blow up.

He was, though, an exception, so violent a mistake that he soon fell down. The rest of us, however, were becoming bigger, but cautiously. We kept our generalized shape. We were lively fore-pawed persons. We ran and hopped quite a lot and quite well, rather in kangaroo fashion, or perhaps it would be wiser to say more like a large Kangaroo-rat or Jerboa. But just on the top of these hoppers' heads, above their eyes there was more of a hump than any kangaroo has ever had. Their heads were tending to become a bit bunchier for their noses were less snouty. Watch their eyes, too. You'll now see that they are beginning to tend to work in pair. That's what we call binocular vision. It looks a small thing to do. But of all the strange inventions these wonderful ancestors of ours worked on themselves, this was perhaps the most far-reaching in its results. For by beginning to pull their eyes into line, and no longer letting each eye wander off right and left on its own, they were at last able to see things in the round and to judge what distances objects might be away. We shall see this power growing all the time until we find that with our eyes we have been able to study the stars. Another great advantage and advance that came from their eyes working together, was that their noses ceased to have the first-and-last word as to what's what. A nose is good enough as a judge of dinner or drains. It's little use for any long-range inquiry. So "seeing is believing" is already becoming an unspoken motto among these ancestors. Finally, their hands are obviously getting handier.

So equipped they are pushing inland more and more, finding quite large open plains to wander over. Their eyes, with their new tendency to converge on faraway points, begin to like picking out things at a distance. Their hind limbs, also, more and more like covering the countryside with long hopping treks and swinging-striding hikes. They could and would often now and then lope along, just touching down with their forepaws, as they vaulted over a hummock, a rock or a fallen tree.

"This is better than the sea!" one said to the other.

"Yes, more fun, one sees more. And somehow it seems quite easy, doesn't it!"

He took a flying leap over what was, for him, really quite a big ravine—maybe it was four, five or even six feet wide. After a little hesitation the others all followed, alighting chuckling at the other side. The first one that had led the leap, jumped back and down, diving into the cascade pool on the small ravine floor, then bobbed up, caught a branch that stuck out above his head and, like a gymnast swung himself up onto the bank again among the rest. They all cheered him. They were an athletic team and felt the joy of it.

"My! But we're a fit lot!" shouted one, voicing their general feeling. "I'm sure I could go faster out here than the fastest fish. I feel it in my bones. What fun to streak along with the ground flowing under you like water." And he put his hands on the ground, for there was a stretch of level grass here going for a furlong or more. So, on all fours, he galloped the stretch and back in a matter of a minute or so. His little body seemed to the onlookers to whizz along. When he came back he was flushed with pleasure. As they congratulated him he remarked with complacent diffidence as he wiped the soil from his fingers, "If I had a really strong fore-paw, boys, I'd show you some speed, you bet! Wish I had a less flimsy hand, you know."

"Aren't things going fast enough?" They looked about to see who had spoken. It wasn't any of them and no one else seemed near. Then, through the rainbow which the sun was playing at making with the waterfall's spray, they saw a vast luminous eye regarding them. Or rather, the rainbow was just the shining curve, what we call the iris, of a bright shining, smiling eye. "You really would like a pudgier paw? That means, you know, fewer fingers?"

"Well, I can't see how I can streak along, trying to run on a fringe of feelers like this!" To make his point the potential speed-tracker held up his finger-spread hand.

"True enough," agreed the voice that now sounded like the deep diapason of a big waterfall, "true enough."

"Well then, what am I to do about it?"

"How much do you really want to streak along?"

"Oh gosh, the feeling's so good—instead of all that ambling and loping, hopping and scrambling! Why, when I get going I could clear a ravine twice as wide as that. But you see, I'd have to get up speed and put myself into training just to do that."

"Yes, true enough you would . . ." Then, after a pause, in which the great eye that was using the waterfall rainbow and the beady eye of the questioner questioned each other, "You really want speed more than anything else? You can have it if you wish."

"I'd beat everybody. I know I could. I'd be the speed-maker. Nothing in the water or on the land could keep up with me. I feel it in my bones. I just must let out the energy I feel in myself. I'm sure I'm made to, I'd outdistance everyone. No one could touch me."

"You'd be a bit out of touch with things, wouldn't you?"

"Oh, I'm tired of having to finger over everything, having to make a close-up inspection of every scrap! I like change. I'm a bit bored at the pace we've been going. Let's go places and see things, sort of generally. What's the use of poring over every leaf and flower!"

"Yes, you seem to know what you want."

"To tell the truth," the speed-entrant seemed emboldened by his thought being recognized, "I feel I've been kept ambling about long enough."

"And you feel you've discovered what the goal really is—that's on the level? And that you can get rid of all restlessness just by racing along?"

"Couldn't have said it better myself!" agreed the complacent wisher.

Of course when you are really quite sure, and no one can put you off by questioning whether you really know your own mind, because you feel it in your bones, why then of course, you get what you want. You have to. For that's the way things are made. That's the thing called real faith. But, equally of course, you must take care when your wishes have kept on so long and strong and all-about-one-thing that they begin to be your will. For once things are done, really done—not merely wished but willed with all the will power in you—can they ever be brought back, can they ever be undone?

"You're sure that's what you want?" The question came again.

"Yes, yes! Of course, of course!" coughed the impatient would-be horse, prancing to be off. "Now what have I to do to get fixed?"

"Well," answered Gabriel, "it's clear, isn't it? All you have to do is, of course, just to keep racing about. You needn't think, or puzzle any more. Just give up that kind of thing for good. Gallop off on all fours—you'll certainly pick up speed that way as long as you don't want to pick up anything else, not even an idea."

"You promise me that? It's as easy as that?"

"I do, and it is."

The waterfall took on a deeper note than you'd have thought it had in it—for after all it wasn't really a very big fall, though big to the small crowd around it. And at the same time the sun going behind a cloud, the rainbow vanished. The rest of the group felt a sudden chill and shuddered a little. But the bounder pranced about.

"This is the weather for exercise," he neighed, "good gray day, keen air." And off he galloped. The more he ran the more he liked it. What's more, he seemed to find the land liking to humor him. When he began to run on all fours he was about eighteen inches high and the grassy foreshores of a number of lakes gave him his racing tracks. But under his one urge to be the really big unbeatable racer, he grew, and as he grew he found country that opened out—huge savannas where you could gallop till you'd swept every thought out of your mind, every question out of your head and every trace of that fidgety, tentative feeling out of your paws. They were just fine throbbing bolts with which you hammered the hard earth until it rang like droning, hypnotic music in your ears. He was now obviously getting larger, more muscular. So to carry his weight and to speed that mass along ever faster, his front paws fell into line. Surely then he'd been right? Sure enough, as far as he saw. And of course, like all of us, he saw just as far as he wished. Those fingers which the Group clung to and he'd had, they were just no go for getting along at high speed over the earth. Just in the way, just the kind of useless, springy, weak, touchy things to strain themselves and give you a nasty fall. Those silly little nails, too; they could, of course, pick up a grain or explore a flower—if you ever wished to do such a silly, sissy, time-

wasting thing—but would break and splinter directly you tried
to put any real weight on them. Yes, they must be toughened up.

He'd hardly begun for long to think in that way, when sure
enough two things happened together, and each was precisely
what he'd wanted. First, his fingers did as he'd told them; they
shrank away. "I want just to skim over the earth," he said. "If I
could only touch the ground with one long pole-jumping finger,
that's all I want. All the rest are really in the way. But of course
it would have to be as strong as a pole."

And his hand, obedient as a magic slave, started to do quietly
and precisely that. Indeed the whole of his arms obeyed under the
hands' orders. They drew back into his body and only huge wrists
hung down and out from them grew first four, then three, next
two then one giant pole of a finger.[1] And the nail on the end of it
—that too grew like a corn or wart until he had a hoof like a hammer but as useless as a hammer to do anything but hammer.
Hopping and questing—let alone picking anything up—was now
quite out of the question. Besides now that he'd put himself
down on the ground there was no longer any getting up and having a good look round. No; he was on all fours now for good. He

was level and streamlined as he'd wanted to be, level with the earth. "But you can't look round and see where you are," the others that hadn't chosen yet, called out to him. "Something might be coming up near you and you'd never see!"

"Do you suppose I care," he cried with a neigh of contempt. "That's what I'd give them," and he flung up his heels in the air. "I'd kick them to blazes."

"But if they were too big," they answered.

"Well, you boobs," he whinnied, "then they'd never be able to keep up with me!" and he made off at a canter that shook the earth and flashed him out of sight in a cloud of dust. He was back though in a moment to challenge them again. "Well, who's for the real life! Haven't I used my power of thinking up things well? I don't say we should have left the land. That was a mistake. But I do say that this is the way to conquer it," and he stamped on the earth till the little congregation sitting round felt quite unpleasant tremors up their spines. Several were looking at him with open admiration. But a couple still wanted to know whether this was the real thing, the answer to where one went and what one was meant for.

"Say," said one, "how do you gather your food? You haven't a hand now, how d'you pick and choose?"

"I don't have to," he remarked gaily. "You see. I'm so inventive I've gone beyond you all right along the line. See, I've stretched my neck so I can browse with my mouth right on the food. Where's the need for a hand when you've got your face in the dish!"

"Sounds rather like the whale," one recalled. Aloud he called up to the big four-footer, "But you can't live on grass!"

"But that's exactly what I have learned to do! Oh, you may bet your pudgy paws and finicky fingers, I'm ahead of you inside just as much as outside. I've invented a new digestion as well as a new carriage." And sure enough he wandered off browsing off the grass never having to pick a grain or grub a root.

"He does seem a success."

"He may be the next step."

Half a dozen questioning remarks such as these sprang from the Group. And then, wandering down the long grass alley came another set of big four-footed beasts. "Who are you?" asked the rather frightened little originals.

"Oh, we wandered off while you were watching the one of you that has become a Horse. We think he's not done badly, but not as well as us. True we couldn't beat him at speed but we'd beat him if it came to meeting head on!" The voice ended in a bellow and the huge Bull, for that was what *this* protomammal had chosen to become, flourished his great horns. "Your horsy friend, he can kick very nicely, but really he has to play the coward most of the time and trust to showing a clean pair of heels to pursuers he daren't face! While with these horns I can send any creature flying over that tree."

"And," remarked his mate, a very fine Cow, "we're more ahead because we've gotten rid of those vulgar primitive ugly front teeth, so unbecoming and useless. You see," and she took a bunch of grass in her mouth, wrapped her tongue round it and drew it in, "you see, that's the way to eat."

"And to enjoy a meal, one should ruminate on it," remarked a second equally sleek cow who sat down, began to chew the cud and disregarded the poor backward still unspecialized mammals who hadn't yet decided that they knew what they should be.

And behind the cattle group came up splendid Stags and lively rock-clambering Goats with their cleverly cleft feet and Deer that moved up the steep slopes as quick as a shadow. A wise goat turned to the little group of originals. "I agree," he bleated a trifle condescendingly, "that the Horse, with that hoof of his, has gone a bit too far. But why you couldn't have had the sense to make this clever kind of compromise," and he looked complacently at his cleft feet, "this neat, true balance between that horse's clubfoot and your silly jack-of-all-trades flipper—well, the more I look at this cute footwear I've designed, the more I foresee you'll never get anywhere."

The huge concourse of the Herbivores went on rolling by. "My! But there's an impressive number of them, isn't there!" remarked the little Group—now grown distinctly littler. "You needn't choose one model you see! But isn't it about time we did choose to be something definite? Aren't these models better goers than we are—aren't we being left behind? They seem to have the earth just as they like it, sort of kings of creation you might say? . . ."

The Blood-Lusters

"Wait."

They knew the voice, and sure enough, arching over the high tree that closed the vista of the forest glade was their angelic friend, this time bending down so that he rested really very gracefully along the curve of the rainbow.

"Just look down under this arch I'm resting on."

They looked into the shadow and there was something that gleamed like two small fragments from the green part of the rainbow fallen under one of the bushes. But the two splinters of emerald moved of themselves. And then behind them, like a stippled, flowing shadow, someone moved ever so slowly and soundlessly till he was crouched just behind the procession of the Browsers that had been filing along past our tiny Group of still-indeterminates. There had been a mild breeze blowing past both groups and up toward the forest but at that moment Gabriel, resting on his rainbow, waved very gently the furthest tip of the leftmost of his golden flame flight-pinions. At that, the breeze bowed before him and turning, blew back to the Group. It brought, however, something quite other than heavenly assurance on its gale. Even before they found it rank, everyone felt his hair stand on end. The vast procession of ruminants broke into a

stampede panic. The ground shook, the air became dense with dust. But through it our small group heard Gabriel's voice, clear as a whisper in the ear. "You just keep quite still and watch. You will be all right."

And true enough the newcomer paid no attention to them. He was crouched looking after the flying cavalcade. They were certainly glad, right down to the roots of their wilting whiskers, that he didn't, for certainly they couldn't take their eyes off him and he was certainly a far from entertaining puzzle.

Again came the whisper from the great figure watching from above the rainbow, "Keep quite still, don't be frightened. He really is blind to everything that doesn't fear him."

The sinister figure slunk nearer to them. Once or twice he raised his muzzle in the direction where the droves of flying hoofs had made off. And, as he snuffed, he growled with a horrible frustration. But they kept their nerve, bunched in a little huddle near a large bush. And would you believe it, he not only paid no attention to them but when he had come quite close he just rolled over on his back. He not only was obviously quite unaware of them, he had actually lost interest even in the prey that had escaped him. He began to squirm about, for a flea evidently was having a meal off him. And, investigating for that, set him licking himself all over. He groomed away now as if his life depended on it.

"Look at that tongue," said the whisper.

It, too, was more interesting than reassuring. True, it was a tongue but it was covered, the tongue itself, with what looked like small teeth. And, as it shot out to currycomb its coat, it showed alongside—real teeth—and they were even more forbidding. The great fangs flashed in the sunlight. The grooming ended with a yawn which showed the full span of the deadly trap into which this creature had turned its mouth. As the yawn closed, he stretched himself, shooting out his limbs, expanding his paws to the full and from the end of these pudgy, blunted hands, shot out great fangs again, rending talons as dreadful as the teeth.

"Can you trace yourselves in that?" the whisper asked.

The creature was now still, fast asleep on its back. The little crew drew nearer, curiosity conquering fear.

"Do you remember the fellow who crept off after your first deserters had gone back into the sea, the Whale who kept fairly small but just in order that he might use his pent energy to attack and devour the other whales? Well, this is the same horrid clever-stupid blunder made again. This monster was once one of you, just like you. He slunk off first of all when the first of the Browsers and Speed-Runners began to think they had found out how to live well and what life was for. And he was sure he had them caught and beat. For he was cunning enough to see they were suckers, and he was foolish-tough enough to make up his wish-mind that he would live off them.

"Live off them?"

"Look at his tools! He's equipped himself like that to be a wretched bloodsucker. That's all he is! Those teeth were once

like yours, that tongue as sensitive and soft as yours. And those wretched murderous paws—what are they but your delicate, questing, inventive little hands turned into a rip-murderous weapon and good for nothing else. You see, he's just a helpless parasite running about on them. Some of your erstwhile friends are too fast for him now, and others with their horns too much of a match for him. He's always in danger of starving outright. For of course, as you've seen in the cases of the Sea-Loungers and the Browsers, his insides have backed him up with his outside choices. That's the wonderful thing about the gift that the Supreme Giver packed up within you. All you have to do is to wish and keep on wishing and then the countless things, the innumerable changes that are necessary to make your wish work, why they are done for you. You can't understand how wonderful that is. I only faintly can, and not all the while. But when I do then I stand before That Light and I'm lost in reflection, every photon of me flashing back, reflecting not all His Splendor (that no being He has made may do) but all I can contain."

And suddenly, above the rainbow, as though all its five bands of color had leaped up in one wave and become the pure, original dazzling white, there came a blaze they dared not look into. But in the light of it everything glared with beauty and even the sleeping Tiger shone with striped splendor and in his starved sleep purred like a contented kitten. The light modulated to bearability, the tiger fell into a deeper stupor as the whisper went on.

"If you could see into that poor self-mutilated paw as I can, right to its nerves and sinews, you'd see that it's all bound up and deformed, made captive and manacled by its obsessive wish to live on others and never to live by its own invention and questing, never to cherish and caress but always to destroy. If you could look as deep as I can, you'd see that his digestion now is that of a helpless diet-imprisoned invalid. Give him your widely-spread, richly-varied, healthy diet, it is death to him. Unless he can get his pure meat-and-blood feeding—why the poor creature begins to get fits like a starveling baby.[1] It's not that he won't eat the harmless plenty the Giver has given to you all—he just can't—it's become poison to his now poisonous murderous nature. And," the whisper took a deeper tone until it seemed the sound wave of sorrow itself, "he can never—by himself—get out of his self-laid trap now that he has turned himself into a deathtrap for others. Again, if you could see with my eyes, you would see that the passion he roused in order to make himself the parody of life which he has become, that passion has had (had to have) another physical bodily effect on him. When the All-Giver gave you—and him— the power to keep alive all the while whatever the weather, that you might learn all the while and learn to know Him in dark days as in light,[2] he gave you a marvelous packet of obedient energies in little nuts of flesh hidden up and down your bodies. The one in your throat—it is shaped like a little bridge—is a wonder. For it not only helps keep your bodies warm but it kindles your minds

too. Indeed, it is a true bridge between your minds and your bodies. And working with it, as a thermostat for your minds and bodies, are a pair, even smaller, right down in the middle of your backs. Those are the little living batteries he designed for you and planted in you. They can drive you against the tide, against the down-going current of things. They are the powers that reply to your persistent wishes, translating your settled mood into bodily build. But, also, when you have made this choice, then these batteries drive you along the track and at the grade you have chosen—up or down. Well—or I should say *ill*—this poor self-made cripple has actually reversed that rising balance. For him it now points down. He can never persist and think and strive patiently, as you can, with your bridge-gland to help you in your throat and back you up with the bodily habits and shapes it can lay down for you. No, he has made his glands of anger and attack so large that his bridge-gland of persistent effort has shrunk. He can then never think himself out of his mess. Indeed, he now can never stop the memory-obliterating attacks of anger that come on him. He is really no more than an automaton of rage. If he isn't in a temper he's in a torpor. He's gone back to be a kind of psychotic Saurian as far as his conduct is concerned—utterly unteachable, utterly unable to learn."

They looked with increasing pity at the great lithe body, so supple, so strong, so really helpless and hopeless.

"Of course," went on the whisper, "he couldn't live if all tenderness utterly left his imprisoned heart. Always by the Utter Mercy there comes the recurrent moment in every life-turn, when tenderness must come in that creation may continue. The mother tiger must be infinitely tender at least to her cubs. But she cannot trust even the father. The trinity of compassion has already vanished here. Against him she turns with fury as though he were her prey; and she has reason, for he, toward his young, is a monster.

His passion for flesh is stronger than his own procreative love. He would eat his own young and so destroy the race-life in him which he has degraded."

"Is there no hope?" suddenly asked one of our little Group who had crept nearest the sleeping brute.

"I don't know," slowly said the Archangel. "I do know that there is a way down. I do know that one of your lot who went some of the way so as to become like him, just a blood-hypnotized killer, went right back into the sea-shallows. He, too, is following the whales to the ultimate sludge abyss. For those Seals (you can hear them from this spot barking on the shore)—yes, they broke off from you. First they tried to become killers of their own kind, then they tired. Now they are more than half into the sea and their bodies are showing the first signs of turning into fish bodies. No, they will never find their way here. And indeed, one of the Browsers, too, he also has become a kind of Seal and he, the Manatee,[3] now lies awash, swept by the invisible current against which all of you must always swim, swept back into that great gulf of bitter water which is always ready to swallow everything to which it gave birth."

There was another silence, the surrounding stillness only broken by the sound far away of the tireless ocean gnawing at the beaches and the straining cry of a stranded seal.

"I don't know," again the great figure spoke, "but you should know that the Browsers and the Blood-Lusters have now tied

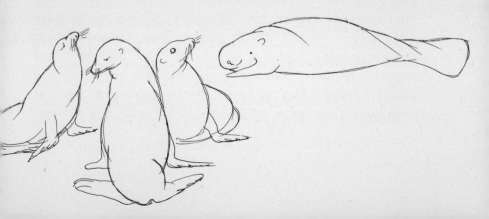

themselves together in so dreadful a knot that my mind cannot see how it may be unloosed. Because they shrank from feeling the need and pain of what they had yet to know, the pull of what lies ahead, unknown, because they wouldn't hunger for something beyond all appetite, they now can't live unless each lives through the other. The Blood-lusters, of course, long for the blood of their prey—once their brothers. Indeed, now they are so depraved all through, they die if they can't be so fed. But the Browsers too—they need dreadfully, helplessly, to be stalked, hunted, shaken from their torpor. For they are dying inwardly, dying in the cold of their own failing vitality. Out of this deadly frost they can only be roused by terror of the lurking beast. He alone can stir in their sluggish blood an excitement that drives off the fatal chill spreading from the heart. They have found life so easy that at length it is not worth the living. Their torpid bodies—though they seem swift and strong still—are so lacking in true liveliness that they can't resist attacks from creatures far too small for you to see—but more deadly than the Flesh-Tearers themselves. When the Browsers are chased by the Blood-Lusters the blood of the chased does course, if only from fear—their vitality does rise for a moment. So they are saved from an inner infection, a far more sweeping destruction by plagues they could never see nor escape, plagues that leaping invisibly from victim to victim would destroy not merely a laggard here and there but the whole pack, the whole species. Yes, in order that they may live now at all, they always have to have beside them an enemy threatening them."[4]

Of course all this was getting almost as far above the heads of the Archangel's audience as were the tips of his tallest flight-pinions above their eyebrow whiskers. Indeed, their attention, which was always more easily caught by something that could be seen than by just talk, had wandered off. They were watching a distant group of Browsers which, having forgotten their fright, had relapsed into

feeding and as they mowed and mopped up the grass were saunter-
ing toward them. At that moment the tiger woke, too. He was wide
awake in an instant, crouched down, waiting. The wind now
favored him—their smell had roused him, his had not yet reached
them. They continued to come on. Their eyes fixed on the ground,
they did not see more than a yard or so beyond their noses. And
one was so greedy that, to keep his nose constantly in the fodder,
he shuffled along on his knees, only getting up, and then slowly
and stiffly, when he had finished a lush patch and had to look
for another thick bed of grass. Suddenly with a roar the tiger
was on them. He had been too impatient and those who were on
their feet managed to make a getaway. But the crawling glutton
was caught. As the poor victim was dragged out of sight, the
group saw that on its knees were great callouses and the knee joints
were swollen and infected. The creature had already half-turned
itself into a cripple.

"I know it's shocking," remarked Gabriel as soon as the Group
which had been chattering with fright could attend to him, "but
you see it's a kind of pruning, really. The Browsers want to become Food-Scoops, like the Whales. And, by nipping off the
scoopier ones the Tiger is really keeping the others from falling
into that fatal sleep-walking that can only end in death."

"Yes," replied someone, "I suppose if you're falling to sleep in
the snow, you should be glad if you're pinched awake—even if
someone pinches so hard he nips off the frost-bitten end of your
toe."

"But then that would mean, wouldn't it, that there's more of
a chance for the Blood-Lusters than for the Browsers, the Mowing-
Machines?" The question rose from a rather slow loping little
person, who was always getting left behind by the nimble because
he would always be stopping and gazing at a bud—not nibbling
it but just looking at it and then perhaps poking it with his finger

to make it sway—or sometimes even looking right away into the distance lost in some kind of brown or blue study.

The Archangel turned wholly toward him—gave him all his attention. And when an AA does that then the person who is attended to finds himself literally in the limelight, in the floodlighting. The little behindhand fellow was covered with confusion for really he was thinking aloud to himself, indeed, he had forgotten even himself and the Angel. He was indeed doing something that he'd been on the point of doing once or twice before but had never actually fallen into. He wasn't thinking of what would happen to them themselves—or how awkward it was to have people around who turned themselves into death traps or how the devil you were to avoid falling back into the sea or becoming a Mowing-Machine yourself, or even an automatic death trap. He was actually thinking of the great waterlogged lost-at-sea mammals. And he was wondering whether anything could be done for them, whether they could ever wish themselves back into freedom, or even perhaps, as a last desperate outcome, be wished back by someone else, by someone perhaps who actually gave them some of his wish-power which he hadn't squandered, some of the wish-power which he might have spent on himself.

And the Archangel, seeing that this member of the Group was lost in that strange new baffling, bright tanglewood called the world of thought and ideas, and seeing interiorly what those thoughts were, seeing that the light of his great angelic attention might stop this exploration going on, put out his hand, shrouding the manikin figure from the heavenly radiance that streamed from himself, and took the small person in the hollow of his palm. It both protected him and also permitted the tiny slow, squeaky voice, as in a sounding chamber, to reach the rest and to arrest their attention.

"Perhaps then they might both be saved somehow, somehow?" The little strain of thought gave out in silence.

The Archangel put him down gently at the back of the Group where he wished to be. Then Gabriel drew himself up to his full height until his face seemed to have gone right on into that ultimate blue that is so deep and dark that it seems to have drawn up into itself all the light of the sky. After a long time he turned back again. "I don't know," he said. "I am let see much, but not the end. I can see there are many ways down—gently slippery slopes, sudden precipices, slow sucking morasses. But there is only one way up, dark, rocky, thorn-caught, narrow, very steep."

"But," and again it was the slow one from the back of the meeting, "but if someone should miss it—fall off it—could they not find it again?" The squeaky voice was anxious almost to panic. Somehow, though, you felt—at least the AA did—that the panic was not for the speaker himself. "I don't know . . . I don't know" . . . The great voice was now tolling like a passing bell. "I don't know," it cried again with the sorrow of an almost unbearable uncertainty. "I don't know." The light of the glade sank to that strange rather dreadful livid hue which the air takes on when at noon an eclipse begins to eat like a disease into the bright disk of the sun. Again the sigh sounded through the stillness and the group shuddered to the marrow of their spines. "I don't know. However, *I don't know that it might not happen*. It all depends, depends . . ." And as that last word was repeated the light began to swing to and fro, as though the sun itself was being swung like a blazing censer before some invisible, inconceivably high shrine.

"It all depends . . ." Again there was the feeling through the air and the earth itself as though some final issue was being raised before a judgment so inscrutable that no pleading could be offered. "It all depends." And this time there could be no further doubt—

there was being made some act of final trust, some offering of final confidence.

The Group looked up and they saw their friend standing right on the keystone of the rainbow. All was dark underneath. In the womb of the arc of iridescence was nothing now but a writhing cloud of complete blackness. The huge figure, however, rose on and up through belts of ever-growing clearness until they could just see his face was turned toward a point beyond where they could look. At that instant suddenly, again, but now even more terribly bright, that Glare flashed down on the upturned face smiting it into pure flame.

Blinded, they put their little snouts on the earth. They could hear a panic howl of dread from the great blood-beast in the thicket, howling as it does when flame smites eyes and muzzle. In the silence after that they heard still more faintly and for the last time, "It all depends, depends, depends . . . This one thing He permits me to tell you. Not on us who see, not on us who adore, not on us who are beyond all doubt even when we own our ignorance, beyond any fear even when we feel for your fate—not on us, but strangest and subtlest of all the sublime choices, on you the weakest of the weak, it all depends on you. Can you do it? Will you do it? He has not shown me though I reflect Him. He will not tell me though I announce and record for Him. But He has told me that you could do it, if you would make the final act of daring—if only you will not fear to be weak, if only you could trust Him, not in His obliterating strength but in His tenderness—if only you could trust in Him to work in weakness through you, for you, who still don't know Him, and for that poor thing that now can only fight against Him."

The Air-Walkers

The group ambled and hopped along for another million of years and miles exploring space and time, and still not really sure they were getting anywhere.

"I say," suddenly remarked one of the littlest—for they were not all quite of the same size, and this one was distinctly down at the small end of the scale, while his little voice squeaked right up at the top, "I say, I've thought up an idea!"

The rest stopped and looked at him.

"It can't be very big if it fits inside you!" said a largish rather beaver-looking person who was certainly on the pompous side.

"Anyhow it's original, and I bet I've found the way out from all this mazing, plodding and burrowing."

The rest were interested.

"It's a high-up idea," said the small one in his intense squeak. "You see, we've seen what comes of trying to go back and lounge it out in the ocean."

There was a pretty general grunt of agreement.

"We have also seen what comes of trying to make the land into a sort of sea for sailing over at top speed and feeding off it as though it were all seaweed."

Several persons at that point said, "Hear, hear!" For even if you aren't certain where you are going, it is always a little encouraging to know that other people's solutions that seemed smart —and you were thought slow for not adopting—didn't work out after all. So encouraged, the small one thought the time had come for a question.

"We have tried the sea and we have tried the land?"

"Yes," came a sort of hesitant murmur.

"So now what remains?"

"What?" came a wavering echo.

"Why," said the small one with his beady eyes twinkling, "why the air!"

"Oh, don't be so fresh and clever," several people grumbled.

And one added, "That's the birds' business. Besides, have they done so very well? I thought we weren't to lose our hands any more than we were to lose our heads on this long trek—at least that's the sense of the story—to me." There was a general assent to this diagnosis.

"But why should we lose our hands?"

"Well," said one squirrel-like person who had long had a habit of putting up for the night in burrows, "I often find in my burrow a little owl—he and I get on all right. But I've watched him, wings aren't really much fun or use. He has to use two of his fingers, which he's grown to a huge size, and out of these he has to grow long feathers. We can't grow feathers. Don't you remember when we gave up our scales they were turned into hairs?"

"Yes, I know all about that," replied the small one. "We've let the scales grow into hairs and the birds let their scales grow into feathers. I agree I don't feel any capacity in me to grow feathers and don't want to."

"Then how are you going to fly?"

The little one held up his very little hand. "Ladies and gentlemen, observe my hand." They did. "You see in between each

finger where it joins the palm is a small bit of almost what you might call webbing?"

"Yes," they said not very encouragingly, for all this seemed hopelessly off the point.

"Do you mean to suggest that out of those little gussets you're going to grow a sail, a wing!"

"Precisely." They all laughed. "And what's more"—and his little voice was sharper than ever, so you could hardly hear it because he was so cross—"I'm going to sell my hand and yet have it, make it into a wing and yet keep it as a hand." This seemed such sheer boasting that all the others almost booed. "Yes, I will," he hissed back and hopped off.

They didn't see him for ages.

"Bet he dived off a cliff and knocked the wind out of himself trying to walk on the air and fly with his hands," said the others whenever they thought of him.

And then one evening, when they were all sitting about in the warm dusk—rightly called the blind man's hour—someone remarked, "That's a late bird not to have gone to roost yet."

"And he looks half drunk from the way he's flying."

"Lost his way home," said a third.

And evidently he was so lost that he was ready to ask the way of anyone. He eddied and wobbled nearer and finally, with a queer

little flop, alighted on the ground. Everyone gathered round and then out of what looked like the struts of a collapsed parachute who should peer up but the little one.

"I've done it," he squeaked, "I've done it and left you all behind. I have found the way out; it's up, up into the air, into the sky. That's the way that those mutts who went back into the sea were seeking, that's the really open speed-country which the other later mutts thought they were getting into when they learned to gallop."

They were all more impressed than they wished to show, so one said,

"Show us your invention, old fellow!"

"Wait a moment," replied the little one. With difficulty he crawled onto a stone but, once there, suddenly he put out his arms. The rest drew back, the nearest ones were nearly under a sort of umbrella.

The little one squeaked with pleasure at their surprise. "You see, though I hardly expect you'll be able to believe it—that outer rib of my wing is just my little finger which I've grown right out from its useless just-hanging-on position till it rounds off my figure quite nicely." And he spread himself at full span. Certainly it was rather an achievement.

"But what have you done to your face!" said someone peering up at him.

"Oh well," he answered, "haven't you stick-in-the-dusts yet tumbled to the fact that when we make inventions, when we really wish up things, then our whole body backs us up? Remember our big feathered friend who was always giving us good advice? Remember what he told us? Though I say it who shouldn't, I was the only one who saw the point and climbed into the sky." He smirked and swept himself a bow with his big vans. "Didn't he keep on telling us that we really had nothing more to do than to wish with all our hearts, minds and wills and our bodies would follow suit—and would have to give us all the fittings and fixings we'd need to carry through our big idea?"

"Yes," they agreed, "yes, I suppose he did."

"Well, you see, I've now gone ahead in every way—you mustn't mind my telling you the truth—otherwise you see, I can't answer your questions, can I? I'm a cut above you in every way. For just because I fly, just because the air is now my way of getting about, I have to have more energy. I'm much more alive than all of you creepers and crawlers—I have to be. So I have to have high energy food. I live in the air and by gum I'm so ingenious that having done that damn clever thing I go one better and actually live on the air. See my chest!" And he stuck it out further than ever a prima donna has been able to do. "On that, of course, I've put the huge muscles I need to wave these wings," and to show them his power he sent a draught of cold air over their backs. "But, conversely"—he was now quite in the lecturing style— "conversely I, of course, enlarged the interior of my chest and so have lungs proportionate to the effort I have to make. That means —I trust you follow me—for I own I'm pretty quick for you— that I just must have more air. More air to travel through, means more air needing to be taken in." And he squeaked at his own not very nimble joke. "So my face, which is really improved when you understand its present contours, is just to let me breathe the better."

"Your ears are a bit disproportionate, too," remarked someone.

"Not at all." His voice in spite of its thinness was quite pompous with dignity. "Not at all. I have developed these proportionately, precisely. And like all proper development, once you get used to the scale, and are let in on the reason for it, you will see how beautiful they are."

They were certainly odd, as convoluted and expanded as his nose and mouth.

"Air again," went on their self-illustrating lecturer. "Air is my element. I'm a creature of the air, a thoroughly new creation. In fact, I hold it as demonstrable that I'm the final, the only right answer to creation, to the riddle that we, the forefingers of life, have been set. So I actually take in, not only my fuel but also my bearings from the air. You wouldn't be able to understand it if I went into the details, just because you are too coarse, too undeveloped even to hear, much less to understand, what I'd be talking about. But I can tell you that I've made as much progress with my voice as with my ears—perfect co-operation you see, playing on myself, conducting myself as a sort of orchestra."

"Your voice sounds more squeaky than ever," retorted a rather bass-voiced rat.

"Ah, that's just what I would expect from a totally untrained ear," came the complacent answer. "As a matter of fact, you can't make all the sounds I make—and of course you can't hear them. But now listen to me and you'll have to own that this is real triumph—I have in my throat no less than three ways of making intelligent sounds. You can hear this voice with which I'm speaking to you."[1]

And they had to own that, though high and shrill, it was carrying.

"Also, besides that, I can speak to my family in a tone which you can't hear—and that's always a convenience when you're with people who may only misunderstand what is well above their heads. But—and this I know even you will have to own clinches the question of my superiority—I am all the while—even now—sending out a note you can't hear but I can. That's what's called echo-sounding—it allows me every moment even when flying at

high speed to know where I am. I can fly through a thickly tangled bush and if there is room for my neat body and clever wings to weave through—you can be sure I'll never run into anything, however dark it is. Dark makes no damn difference to me," and he hopped into the air, danced up and down, soaring in and out of low-sweeping twigs of a tree and in and out of bushes till they were dizzy trying to watch him. The dark made it impossible anyhow to trace him. But all the while they heard his triumphant squeak, "Do you believe me now? Look at me! Look at me! I can see with my ears and could fly perfectly well blindfold."

When he alighted and was eating an insect or two which he'd caught on the wing, one of the most observant and least restless of the group remarked, "You certainly do seem to have bought yourself a fine bag of tricks, but I notice you have had to pay."

"What do you mean?" the Leather-Wing was offended.

"Well, first of all, that hand of yours now really isn't much use any longer, is it? 'Cept as a grapple to hold onto the air. And secondly, as far as I can see, and I have fairly good night-sight, your eyes have gone to pieces."

"Oh well, I really don't need them."

"They don't get in the way at all then?"

"Oh, of course, I find it better not to be out in too strong light —I mean it's a bit dazzling."

"You mean that now you can only creep out at dusk and bob up and down in the air catching flies. You really can see nothing. As for all this hearing by echoes—that merely tells you whether

you should give a wide berth to objects that have no other interest for you save as ugly possibilities of collisions!"

"Well, what's the use of the day? The insects I like to feed on are, most of them, only out at night. And as to long views, I always failed to see much use in them! I'm doing far better than any of you. You can't deny I've gone up in the world!"

"And what do you do all day?"

"Oh, I sleep. I'm quite ready for that after a brisk night's hunting. I get into some quiet dark nook and just hang up. Watch . . ." and he first swung himself into the air and then, catching hold of a hollow branch above them by thumbnail hooks on the tip of his wing, swung head-over-heels and hung there upside down.

"The blood must go to your head like that!"

"And a good thing, too," came the sleepy answer. "Tell the truth, flying's such fine sport, and hunting on the wing's such fine game that, as I've said, I always feel ready, as I do now, to turn over and turn in when I've caught my meal."

"But what do you do when the nights are cold and the insects have all died off till next spring?"

"Ah," came a sleepy voice from the dark crotch up in the tree above their heads. "There, you see, I'm still further improving! I can now sleep not merely through every one of your blazing and boring days, I can sleep right through the inconvenient winters, as cosy as, as cosy as . . ." And the voice dropped off into a little wheezy snore.

The group looked round at one another. For, as one of its last spokesmen has said, they had very good night-sight. Some were impressed. One lot stole off to get lessons. They became the Flying

Foxes and such like skidders and scooters on the down slopes of the air. One went further. He not only became a full bat, he was determined to get more energy—for it was clear that flying was so taxing he must have more. He it was who became the Vampire, the black-winged night-horror that gently lights on his victims, sucks their blood while they sleep and leaves them to die.

But on the whole, the reaction of the Group was one of puzzlement at this departure. They hardly knew what to make of such an utterly odd and unexpected ascent. As they looked about, vaguely wondering what would happen next, there over the edge of the plain, calm and wonderfully beautiful rose the full moon, light and soundless as thistledown floating in the sun. Its glow of amber lit the earth and the sky making a lovely arc of light. At the same time, across the arch of heaven appeared a long gleaming cloud like a mantle of silver, fluted with pale gold. As it reached down it took the moon into a fold of its drapery, holding it like a large shining pearl. The manikin meeting, cricking necks still further, looked up to where the cloud itself ended at the very zenith. Two particularly bright stars looked down from there and fringes of smaller gleaming ones spread around.

"Oh!" they exclaimed. For, faintly etched in fire, they could make out the face of their friend.

"Well, what do you think of the latest wish-choosing?" he remarked in a voice as gentle as the night.

"It's mighty ingenious," they answered.

"Yes, perhaps the most ingenious of all," Gabriel reflected. "But it's just ingenious, really that's all. Long before I first spoke to you all out on that old mudbank, before there was this lovely sun and star sky, there was a cold-blooded Lizard, a Saurian, who managed somehow to do precisely what these Bats have now done —and he was much bigger. And he did it precisely the same way, stretching out his fingers and growing the web between them till he had a skin-wing. It's he who is going to. be called the finger-winged, the Pterodactyl.[2] It's no use repeating past inventions. Besides, with your brains you ought to be able to think up something better than a numb-skull Lizard could contrive."

"It seems to me," followed up one of the group, "our little bat friend has given up a good deal, hasn't he?"

"Yes, but does that really matter?" Gabriel questioned. "If he really did find out where the way you are all going leads to, if he really could see where the goal lay, then would it matter what else he lost or left behind?"

"No, I suppose it wouldn't. No, I suppose it would be worth while . . . Anything would be worth that."

"Even going on waiting, going on not being sure?" Gabriel gently goaded.

"Yes, I suppose even that would be worth while . . . Yes, it would."

"You see that?"

"Yes, yes," the spokesman felt somehow he was giving his word, "Yes." The third "Yes" sounded like a verdict and in a way it was. Anyhow, suddenly the speaker brightened, "Oh, I see . . . he just didn't go that far. He was blind as a bat."

"Then. you think even the air isn't the way out, the way to real freedom and full creative ease?"

"Well, it doesn't look as though it was, considering what he's done with it." The spokesman and the questioning archangel, the one from below, the other from above, considered the torpid little creature hanging between them in a cleft of the tree.

"You think," went on Gabriel, "there might still be another way, still harder to find, and harder to climb? And you're still willing to wait and fumble and trek along?"

There was a long silence. Then the wisest spoke for the meeting with a sigh, "Yes, we're ready."

The white sculptured drapery of the long cloud melted away in the sky. The stars drew back till they were only points of faint fire in the deep of night. The moon sailed free across the sky.

With another sigh the little group gave a shudder or two in the chilling air, curled themselves up and went to sleep preparing for another unknown day.

Part II

THE LAST-CHOICERS

The Scene Gets Set for a Showdown

The scene hasn't shifted much. There in the foreground are groups of really fine trees, trees just like the ones we know. They stand round the borders of great sweeps of park land and prairie, great billowing plains that roll on till they rise to hills on the horizon. Green meadows in the foreground, silver rivers stitched across the green, the green turning gradually to mountain blue and this blue, when it gets deepest in color and highest up, dazzlingly edged and mounted with snow fields brighter than the white clouds that keep on forming on the blue sky.

Certainly nothing looks dramatic or boding. Nonetheless, there can be no doubt we have come into a change. For one thing the climate is brisker. That snow line comes farther down than it did. In fact, almost every range now is finished off with this white porcelain roof and there are a lot of ranges about—more snow

to fall and more mountains for it to sit on. The summers are hot but short, the winters long and sharp. The sky heaps together fat clouds and then, when they have burst, the blue that is left is cold, the wind keen. If you are vigorous you call it bracing. If you're slack you growl that it's damned cold. Perhaps the clearest way of putting the change is that everything seems becoming more distinct, definite, final.

Instead of long level lagoon-edged lands quietly melting into broad shallow seas, the land is pushing up into steep ridges and peaks and the sea replying by becoming deeper as it loses spread. Perhaps when you'd swept your eye right round the landscape you might begin to wonder whether the scenery wasn't being shifted for a new act, put into a new key for a more rapid movement. And perhaps you might risk a guess that it was being put ready for a showdown of some sort, perhaps a finale.

The other thing you'd notice—though perhaps this would take more looking into—would be some sort of change in the animals. Almost all the mammals that were about during the first meeting of the Group have gone for good or gone and changed into something quite unlike what they were then. In short, nearly all had their wishes. And as we've seen, they turned themselves into some shape that would save further trouble by letting them get just the one thing which they were sure they wanted—always some form of stupidly easy living. They spent their wishes in trying to find a save-trouble, fool-proof, get-you-food-without-thinking body. And having found it, or made it, and wanting to be such a fool whose one wish is not-to-have-to-trouble-to-understand, naturally, having gotten into something as ingeniously tied up as that, they couldn't get out. That's the real trouble with fool-proofing things. When they go wrong or you want to make them do anything except their fool-proof trick, then a fool is the last person to be able to put them right. In point of fact, when that happens you have to send for a very clever person indeed ... who's proof against you, the fool.

Indeed, as the screen lifts and the scene changes slowly it's now becoming clear that only one small lot remains . . . who haven't yet spent their magical wishes and turned themselves into too-clever-by-half-contraptions. This lot still looks something like the first Group that Gabriel visited on the mudbank among the Dinosaurs some seventy to eighty million years ago. That at least we can see—this bunch has managed to keep its hand and not turn it into some silly gadget such as a hoof or a dirty weapon such as flesh-ripping claws. And not only has it managed to keep its hand by holding onto its handiness, it has hauled in its nose and also kept its teeth from getting out of hand by becoming tusks and so trying to prove that hands didn't matter.

It would seem then that this lot, though it looks far from distinguished, may have considerably more in it than meets the eye. For this nondescript clan may prove to be even more interesting just because it still has packed up inside it all the unspent wish-power that we've seen bursting out and flying about and making more-or-less monsters of all the other warm-blooded animals. Another thing is unmistakable as this increasingly definite age comes on . . . There isn't a single original idea left in the rest.

That does not mean all their wish-power has been spent. Indeed, it would be better for them if it had been. What is happening to them is odder, more magical, and grimmer than that. The only way we can put it is to say that the wish in every case seems (after the wisher has told it to go ahead) to take the bit in its teeth. It insists on going on wishing itself to be bigger and bigger all on its own and for itself. Finally, there's a third thing to notice about this new time, a thing that makes everything more critical for everyone—*things are going faster*. It takes less time for wishes to come true and that means, of course, that when they get on their

own they bring the unhappy wisher who first wished them, quicker
and quicker into a more hopeless mess. So in this second part of
this strangest of all strange transformation acts we have to keep
our eyes on two things: We must watch the small lot that hasn't
yet wished—seeing the final lures and temptations which attacked
it, the temptation to give up general readiness and open-minded-
ness; the wish to turn yourself into something definite and final
which will henceforth simply do the one thing you like doing and
nothing else. And, at the same time we must watch what's happening (for it did happen at the same time, only a few million
years ago) to the unhappy animals whose silly wishes were still
going on growing in them and driving them to extinction.

First, then, let's get the Yet-To-Wish contingent in our mind's
eye. It is not as numerous as it was—and the people in it, nearly
all of them, tend to be larger in frame. Their heads are becoming
rounder and bump up at the top; their snouts are shorter; their
ears are curling and getting small; their eyes are beginning to swing
still more toward the front so that each eye sees exactly what the
other one sees. For now their eyes have to work twice as hard;
they not only have to take the place of their noses, which now are
well on the way to becoming politely obsolete, more for impress-
ing other people than for giving information to their owner. Their
eyes have to do all the accurate checking-up which formerly was
done by swiveling your large cup-shapd ears and so estimating
where a stranger might be standing. The laying back of one's ears
till they look like a piece of tidy hair-dressing means that hence-
forward the ear can do no more than say, "There's a noise somewhere about. Please, eyes, would you see what it means."

These creatures, who depend now increasingly on seeing, are also
beginning to walk about quite a bit. Though they like a tree as their
house and home they are continually coming down onto the ground
and toddling and trotting about as children do in their first years.

But the real thing to notice about this group is their hands. Not so much for their shape; they're not so very striking, these queer fringed little paws that have changed so little. Watch what these hands can do. They are at work nearly all the while. They groom each other's coat of hair when there's nothing better to do.

But most of the time the early possessors of hands are busy picking up, testing, turning over, twisting things around, arranging and rearranging everything they can touch. On the ground they make patterns in the dust or the mud with twigs and flowers and bright stones. And then, taking some of their playthings with them up the tree—when they climb there to roost for the night—it is great fun to drop the pebbles onto the ground below and watch them fall and bounce and roll away. How these lively little creatures must have chuckled and crowed as they did that—and then clambered down, picked up their stones again and started another game, seeing whose stones would hop farthest when you dropped them.

The Dancing Danglers

But some found after a time, that getting down onto the ground and spending most of your time there and only using the tree as your support-point, your base and your safe dormitory, wasn't the best way to have the most fun. After all, this thing of walking, walking well up on your hind feet, was none too easy.

Moreover, when you went walking, going through the grass and bushes you always had to be taking no end of care. Thorns had a horrid way of running into your feet; snakes would hiss at you and frighten you almost out of your life, shocking you into a very unpleasant vigilance and, even worse, you might see every now and then a pair of those most sinister green eyes watching you. Then you had to shout and stamp and chorus all together, and beat your chest and bump with your stick on the ground and pretend that you were the devil of a he-man and hope that the stalker would take you at your own pretended valuation; meanwhile, all the time you are trying to make, with a sidelong trek that musn't turn into a run, toward the nearest tree, where you might have to sit marooned for ever so long. No, your own tree was best, and you

could have endless fun in it, swinging and trapezing and becoming
the finest gymnast ever. And if you wanted to travel, well, why
go down onto the rough, dangerous ground and toddle about, having to carry that already very heavy head of yours as high as you
could, right up on end on the top of your spine?[1] It made your
whole back ache. While, up in the tree, dangling from a branch
with just a toe touching the trunk now and then, what freedom
and fun! Then you learned quite easily to throw yourself from
one branch-end onto another and so into another tree-span and
then onto another. Why, you could travel through the trees far
faster than the fools that stumbled about at root-and-ground level
and with none of the silly risks they ran. And all the best food
was up here. True, roots and the grass seeds were lacking; but
the fruit that was so much better, that was all here for you. Perhaps
grain made you brainier and certainly ground level made you more
nervously alive, but fruit made you easier. And you could doze for
hours up in the tree whenever you liked—between each course if

you wished—a thing that it would be wildly unwise to do on the ground—now that you had lost the knack of burrowing yourself holes in the earth and were too big to get into the rabbits'. So, to a gymnast, that began to seem the answer—the answer to the wish how-to-take-it-easy-and-yet-get-along.

The sea obviously had been a mistake. Rocked in the bosom of the deep was really to be in the end blunted and eroded (under the excuse of becoming streamlined), and finally digested by the huge bitter maw of Ocean whose other name is Abyss.

Making the earth into a speed track or making yourself into a Mowing-Machine trundling over unending lawns, stoked by the grass that you nibbled down and sucked up—that too was obviously a mistake.

In each case you had lost your hand and in the end were, therefore, helpless. But up in the trees safe at last—surely you had done all that could be expected of you? You had found out where you were meant to live and how! And it was a fine life. Surely a Whale (even when not having his tongue eaten out by a small fellow-whale), was by now so stupid it couldn't even know it was having a slack good time. And the Oxen and Horses—my, how stupid they were! They would come in the heat of the day and stand under your trees to be out of the sun and to avoid some of the Flies, and it was fun to drop pebbles on the Horses and see them start, with no idea how or what had touched them. You could creep lower even, and poke or tickle them with a stick until suddenly they would snort and stampede out into the open and it was so odd that suddenly you would find a queer noise rising in your throat, half a cough and half a swallow—and the others would hear the sound and see what was tickling you and then they, too, would catch this queer chortling and you'd all shake till the tree shook and your eyes would run, and at the end you felt fine and friendly.

It was just as though you'd made a really big find of some sort. No, there could be no doubt about it—you were the cute ones. There couldn't be any question any longer that you had found the way out. In every sense of the word you had come out at the top of the tree. You could practically fly, so you were the equal of that silly little squeaker who hung upside down all the bright day inside the hollow trunk of one of your trees but who was blind in the sunlight and helpless in spite of those hearing aids he'd grown in his ears and was so proud of.

And, the wild joy of living . . . as you

swished through the forest catching sprays of leaves and swinging yourself out into the air and into another tree. You could even scare the leopard—a gang of you—by suddenly rushing above the place where he crouched, leaping where he'd never dare and letting drop on his writhing back large, heavy, prickly fruit.

Oh, there wasn't a doubt of it, you were king of the forest and lord of all the animals. But, of course, you had to keep fit. Those leaps took training. Often you missed, because your fingers were too short to catch hold and take your whole weight on a branch twelve feet away. And then again your thumb would get in the way and you'd slip. And each time you knew with all the gripping wish-power in you, that you must be a gymnast, and nothing else, and that if you were to be as expert as you were determined to be, well then you simply must streamline everything to get there. Long muscular legs must be curtailed, they were too much weight to carry and didn't really help a leap through the branches. Arm-reach and arm-muscle, those were the two things that just had to grow. And out at the end of those long sinewy-thin arms, you must have equally long fingers—for on their fringe of grip your life depended . . .

So the fingers, too, got longer and longer, and the thumb shrank away, till the hand became a kind of hook. You could only gaff it round a branch and swing. You could no longer pick up things neatly. For your fingers were now too long for the palm of your hand.[2] They would actually knock over a small insect or snail you were going to pick up or make a fruit fall before you really had it in your hand. Now your thumb too had no longer a real grip . . . You were losing an accurate grasp of things. More and more you put your muzzle right down on things and let your hands go hang.

The first to go all-out in this way, went off into what is now South America. He is called the Marmoset. He was and still is hardly

larger than the really early mammals. So he found the big trees a terrible problem, for he couldn't hang on even to a small branch with his tiny paws and yet he was determined to tree himself. So he grew real claws just to give him footing. And that meant that he had to become stupid. For as long as his hand, with its neat nails for picking up things, could be used for all sorts of inquiries, it kept on asking his brain questions. When his hands stopped exploring his brain became dull and dumb. So he can only cling on waiting —for what?[3] He remains gentle and shrinking, ready to be friends with anyone who will take care of him, but with a little mind that can no more hold onto a notion than his poor little paws had been able to hold onto the smooth bark of the big trees' branches.

Time passes, again the scene changes . . . A little later nearly all the members of the mammal family tend to become larger.

Then another person after ages and ages thought up another way of being able to hold on in the big trees. Like all the mammals he had a tail. But tails now were becoming little more than a finish to one's back view. Indeed, the most modish people were trying out a shorter-skirted model, one that omitted the tail altogether or only wore it in bob form. But it occurred to this person facing the big trees and disliking coming to earth, that a tail might offer a way out; that, literally, you might turn tail on your problem, still stick safely to the trees, still not face the peril and labor of the ground, the exhaustion of learning to sprint, run and leap with your legs. If the wise thing was not to go ahead but just to dangle and dally about, why then to rock to and fro, making oneself into a swing, that would be the way to amuse oneself without the danger of getting anywhere in particular or putting one's foot in a tight spot.

There came a day when our lot was trekking right along. We were pretty nimble goers. Though, of course, if you are going to stick to all-roundness and general readiness, then you can't be a specialist in any one thing. So we weren't real racers either on the ground or through the treetops. But on the average—through trees and along the open, on the firm level or the squelching swamp or across up-and-down rough-and-tumble moor—we made a fair pace, indeed better, take the all-over time, than any of the speed specialists would have made.

This particular day they were pushing through forest and had—to be honest—stopped to pant and protest a bit as they paused from the continual twisting and swinging of their bodies—when right down in front of their wheezing noses swung a person who seemed at that moment their wish-of-that-moment come true. Our bunch must have felt rather as you would if, looking into the mirror—of course, quite by yourself—you should say: *Oh, I wish I looked like Phoebus Apollo or a movie star*—and suddenly your familiar, all-too-average features began to pull themselves together where they are a bit askew and grow outsize where they are, to put it mildly, too modest and there you would be, so outrageously good looking you wouldn't dare show even your nose outside the door.

But the newcomer was not a reflection. He was a face-to-face fact. Our people were crouched still getting their breath. He seemed so free that exertion seemed impossible for him. He seemed to bob about in the air like a cork on water. With one hand he snatched a fruit, while his left hind foot helped itself to quite a plateful of salad, the other hand casually scratched his ear and the remaining foot waved away a wasp.

"What are you floating in?" called up one of the group very conscious of his own down-drag and avoirdupois.

"Oh," laughed the swinger-aloft, "I can catch on anywhere," and letting the fruit drop and the salad scatter before he'd taken a single bite of either, he threw with super-acrobatic grace a couple of somersaults and once more was swinging and spinning before them. Then they saw that besides four of the most spidery limbs they had ever seen, he had a fifth. His tail had gone on and on till it had become a hand, or at least an immense finger by which he could swing his whole body, flicking it like a string flicks a top. "Springs are better than wings, that's my motto."

"But how did you do it?" They peered up and questioned him, swinging like a queer black flower above their heads.

"Well, as far as I know—but I'm really no go at recalling anything much—I don't hold with brooding—as far as I know, I kept on feeling the tip of my tail as it touched the branch to give me balance, I kept on feeling the wish that it could really take hold. I found I could at last get some sort of grip with the underside of it on the bark. So then I began to put out my tail with all my might—I knew then that was what I wanted more than anything else. Common sense after all, wasn't it. If four paws give you an all-four grip—well, obviously, add one more—and that leaves you when you like with four free hands." All the time he spoke he was swinging and snatching, catching a fresh fruit and letting it fall, lunging at a big butterfly or just cutting aimless capers in the air. Finally, an extra big swing shot him like a rocket out of their sight but as he streaked by our Group saw he hadn't boasted. As his tail streamed along after him, sure enough on the under side of its tip a corrugate end, exactly like a big curled finger.

"My, he can travel," wheezed someone who yet hadn't got his breath fully.

"But where to?" asked another getting ready to push ahead. "Seems to me he never knew where he was facing or what he was up to. He kept on picking things, but nothing I saw ever got as far as his mouth."

"Of course, if you spin like that it is hard to settle down to anything." It was Gabriel who was leaning against a huge sunbeam that sloped down into the forest glade. "Of course he has fun, but at the price you have to pay if you want everything always to be funny—he's completely distracted. For one thing, you see, the way he's got hold of things, his one invention in grip and grasp, is the opposite way to which he should see them. He can really, therefore, never know precisely to what he is attending or to what he is attached—in fact, literally he is always seeing one thing and feeling another—a very confusing state of mind. And of course, too, the moment anything startles him his tail like an uncoiled spring flips him right off into another tree. In fact, as you've seen, just the swing of it, with his body on the end, may send him spinning. He's not got much chance of learning even if he wished to, has he? Naturally, he's learned less and less while he has become more and more efficient as an automatic jack-in-the-box that has sprung loose. Now he's no more than a living coil of springs. His legs and arms, you see, have also become as thin and restless as a spider's. That's why he's called the Spider Monkey. His little mind spins and swivels even more than his swaying dangling body."

Gabriel had to be on the spot again, for at each of these choices, these self-christenings by species after species, he had to wheel down from heaven, as he has to record everything. He mustn't judge, any more than we may. But he has to note everything, witness everything, as we should. Then in the end he will recount everything. We shall see the entire film played over, and He-Who-Alone-is-Able-to-Pass-Sentence, will do so.

The Dangling Drowsers

Our small bunch had just watched the Spider Monkeys swing away in an almost epileptic tension of muscle, when Gabriel whispered, "Look!" As an Archangel's whisper can, when he likes, be even more carrying than any stage whisper—indeed, it can be like a stiff wind—so the dense forest, which our group was watching through his eyes, rippled and laid back all its leaves, sprays and boughs, like a sea under a gale. But though this lot had keen eyes, which were further sharpened by archangelic aid, they still saw nothing—till Gabriel shot a glance from his eye down into a tussock of moss hanging from one of the wind-exposed branches. A glance from an archangel's eye is rather stronger than a strong electric light flashed in your face when you've been in the dark. The moss tussock quivered and there came from it an intensely cross voice.

"Oh go away!"

Gabriel turned away his direct eye-beam, and almost at once our people heard, even through the flutter of the leaves in the wind, a quiet steady snore.

"As he has once more gone under," remarked the Archangel, keeping the branch curled back with a tip of his wing, "he won't be aware if we examine him!"

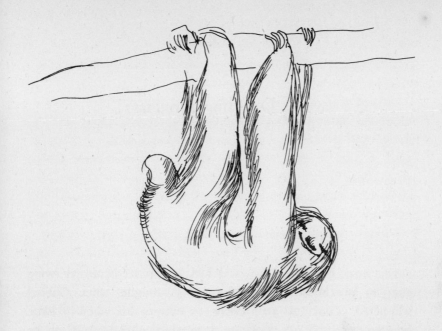

Our crew gathered round close. "My!" remarked one of them, who had put out his hand and touched the tussock, "it's warm, at least this part is, and it's faintly panting. But one just can't see where whoever it is ends and the tree begins!"

"Well," smiled Gabriel, "this is the complete reverse to the answer given by the Spider Monkeys. They've succeeded in getting off so quickly on the hop that they can never learn what it was that set them going. Here's the opposite method, just as extreme in its way—here's Sloth incarnate. Poke him! He's so deep asleep, your little prods won't wake him."

"Oh, but he's got moss growing on him," suddenly screamed an investigator, and looked so disgusted that Gabriel let out a clap of heavenly laughter that did, of course, rouse the Sloth—for of course it is the note that will wake the dead.

"Thunder," it murmured to itself, "I shall get wet. What a nuisance. But it's too much trouble to move."

"You can't have moved for years!" shouted one of the investigators in his ear, with that passion we all have to tell other people things we have discovered about them.

"Do you suppose I didn't know!" came the inevitable answer. Indeed, the Sloth, for a moment, was so pleased at being able to counter-snub its disturber, that it almost came awake. "All you fools," it yawned, "silly creatures—can't count above two! Only two reactions to anything—either fight and squabble or run for your lives! No rest, no poise. Now look at me. I've found out the secret—simple as falling to sleep . . ." and he began gently to snore again. But his audience, more interested than their lecturer, refused to let him pass out. They pulled his hair, and as he couldn't let go of the branch from which his four inter-hooked feet suspended him, he had to wake up again. "Why don't you imitate me?" he went on. "Just stay where you are! Of course you must relax properly . . ." And again he demonstrated so well that another bout of sharp hair-pulling was needed to bring him to.

"Your hands and feet are in pretty poor shape," one of his rousing audience squeaked at him.

"Well," came the same drowsy answer, "I'm never on the ground now, if I can help it. I find being one's own hammock is comfortable, soothing and economical. You'd be surprised how many problems pass you by, if you just hang yourself up and let them go hang." He yawned again, adding, "Excuse me, for not putting my hand before my mouth. It's better employed in letting me depend from it. Obvious, isn't it, that one's hands and feet and nails should be as hooklike as possible. Otherwise one might slip . . . slip . . . when slipping off into sleep . . ." And again he suited the deed to the word.

The group again tugged at his mold-covered hair. And one shouted once more in his ear, "But what's the bright idea about this moss garden you've let grow on your pelt. That kind of trimming's going a bit too far, even for someone who doesn't evidently go much into company. You've relapsed into something hardly better than a half-dead stump!"

Our lot—though with nothing striking about their coats—were already well-groomed and took considerable trouble to keep themselves clean.

"Ah," sighed the Sloth, "I thought that would fool you little fussers. Never heard the motto, 'Rolling stone gathers no moss'? Well, my moss has got considerably more sense in it than meets the eye. As a matter of fact, it fools far sharper eyes than yours— and sharper claws!" He gave a shudder and even half opened an eye. A note of almost urgency came into his voice, "I must ask you particularly to be very careful to replace my leaf bed-curtains now you are going. I have really only one problem and I believe I have him solved. There's an abominable bird. His eyes are sharper even than his claws. He's the Harpy Eagle—an apt name for a feathered fiend. And if he gets a glimpse of me—well, you see I don't specialize in speedy getaways. He looks on me, disgusting flapping fool, as though I were so much meat hanging in his larder. But this moss fools him. So it's my pleasant duty just to stay quite still, hang up and let it grow.[1] I'm pretty sharp, after all, you see! Go on, and mind you leave the leaf-covers as you found them." And, though it was still midday he was fast asleep before they'd let the last branch swing back into place.

"Well," remarked Gabriel, as they looked up to see him standing in the full blaze of the noon sun, giving back flash for flash— giving, indeed, more than he got. "With Spider Monkeys on the one hand and Sloths on the other—what do you think?"

"Looks as though we might still be on the main line?" the Group questioned back.

"Looks it, doesn't it?"

The Wishes That Went on of Themselves

Gabriel waited for a few hundred thousand years to see if his pets would ask anything more. Then he continued, "Of course you've not seen a tithe, no, not 1 per cent of all the different wrong ways already taken by those former companions of yours. You didn't notice them as they slipped and slid off. I did. I guess none of you—or any of us for that matter—will ever be able to imagine all the absurd and perverse ways there are of going wrong, till all of you have given up trying not to, which . . ." and his voice tolled so loud that you'd have thought the whole blue dome was one vast bell and his great golden figure the bell's tongue. . . "Which God Forbid!!"

The little gathering was so shaken that they involuntarily said something which, if it wasn't a hiccup, sounded very like an Amen.

And Gabriel, pleased, went on more lightly. "Seems to me that you've got packed up inside you just an unbelievable number of wrong answers to the one question. For that question has only one right answer."

"What's that?" perked up a smart one.

"Ah, that's asking!" laughed the AA. "Besides, believe me, honestly I don't know—at least in any way that you could under-

stand. I've told you all I've been told. I know there's a right answer
and I know you can give it. I know that's why you've been made.
That's why . . ." and he gave such a sweeping bow with a couple
of his wings that the fragrant wind of it nearly swept them off their
feet. "That's why I am, with all the good will on earth and in
Heaven, your very obedient servant. Hail to you, peculiarly privi-
leged ones. My Master has planned to exalt the humble and
meek."

The audience felt the compliment was just a little mixed—
somehow above their heads and (with all that about humbleness)
below their expectations.

The Archangel saw that, too. "Well," he remarked, rather like
a lecturer who has talked a little too long and now sees that he
should have another slide thrown on the screen, "I think I can
show you a few more false wishes, and that should help you to
find the right one, shouldn't it?" As no one said No, he asked
again, in that easy way we do when we feel the person we are
questioning can only reply Yes. . . . "Haven't you all found that
maybe your main problem's proving to be just this—to have the
patience to keep your nose out of things—and, instead, to put out
your hand? And isn't that just common sense? Don't you see, it's
practically impossible to keep your eye on anything if you have
your nose well down in it?"

Several of the audience, whom it must be owned had begun—
as they often fell to doing when a little bored—to snuff about,
sat up rather stiffly at this and said, "Hear, Hear."

This, of course, encouraged Gabriel. "If you don't keep your
nose out of other people's business, you'll surely get it bitten.
You're being asked no longer to nose but to take a hand!"

At that several did twiddle their front paws quite a bit.

"Good," called out Gabriel, "keep up the five-finger exercises!
And now, look what happens if you don't. If you won't make

contacts in the way you're meant to, with those fingers of yours, you'll make them instead with your teeth. For they follow your nose and since they're not meant for making introductions and discoveries, you simply must have, sooner or later, an end-on collision and smash up. You'll be surprised when you see what happens when you try and make teeth do what fingers should. I'm now going to show you part of that story now that it's becoming rather dramatic. One of your lot's been off on his own quite a while. In fact, he went off when the Browsers made themselves into Mowing Machines. And in that while he's done quite a lot— he thinks—to get his way, have his wish, and turn into his notion of what he holds a smart guy should be. True, he has slipped down from your starting-off position, which was half on hind legs, and which you've kept to fairly well." He ran his eye round the group, and everyone sat up a little more stiffly. "But, till the other day— so to speak—he was a lively enough person, a jolly kid in his way, and one that hadn't taken to horns or to butting people out of his path. Of course he'd given up that hand of yours. He'd turned it into a neat enough forefoot, such as the goats have. Yes, he's sure-footed enough, but he's really lost all true touch now. That cleft foot of his is as little capable of tact as a forked stick! And so, because he can't handle what comes along and gets up against him, he has to chew it. For some little while he's been trusting to his strong outthrust jaw too much—and to his brain too little. He's always getting impatient with the toughness of roots, and then he thrusts and tears, thumps and twists, till he feels his jaw and teeth swell and bulge with the vigor and down-rightness of it all—and he's right, they've gone right down. Look, here he comes."

The Pig Who Chose Punch

Into the glade trotted a Pig. But not that poor, panting over-fed lump of promising bacon, that we now call pig and hog and other terms of contempt. No, he was a trim enough person—dashing, you might say. In fact, the first remark made by our group left no doubt that this was the impression he made on them.

· "What's happened to your whiskers?" they asked.

"They're not whiskers," he answered, a bit tartly. "They're tusks."

"Give you rather a quarrelsome look," said another. "And about time!" he snorted. "Sick to death of being chased about, squealing for mercy and just getting eaten!"

"Of course you can't get up a tree now?" a third questioner put in. "Perhaps you shouldn't have given up your hand?"

"Oh, all this shouldn't and mustn't. I'm sick of it. Besides, you wait, you'll see. I haven't done anything extreme or ill-balanced. Matter of fact, my wife said, just the other day—and it wasn't the first time she's said it, mind you—that I've managed a really smart turn-up to these tusks. You see, though modest, they are of the finest ivory—much cleaner, you'll allow, than hair—and they give a distinctly manly finish to the face, which otherwise might be a trifle blunt and feeble." He glanced rather pointedly at theirs. "Besides," he went on confidently, "the things in themselves are nothing, really. They're just opportunities for skill, for making one's point," and he grinned—though the grin did look a bit brutal because of the tusks. "Fingers aren't the only way of driving home one's point of view," he added, pawing the ground a little irritably with his front left foot.

At that point there suddenly came on the breeze again that sinister smell. Our group took to a handy tree, when, without even a pretense of snooping or stalking, the Tiger walked out again and crouched down to spring on the Pig.

"If he bolts," squeaked someone, "he's just time to make a getaway!" But the Preposterous Pig stood his ground, squealing, not with fear, but, would you believe it, with rage, while his family who had been rooting about in the middle distance made off. The Tiger reared up, just to smash the impertinent porker into a hash. The audience hardly saw what happened. It was quick as a flash. But when over, the Tiger was lying quietly spread out like a rug, not a breath left in him, and—to be painfully frank—hardly any guts. The Pig was wiping his tusks on a near-by tussock.

"Yes," remarked Gabriel, who had been looking on with a very noncommittal air, "that should show you people what energy and dash you've got locked up inside you. He was quicker than that overgrown cat and wilier—ran in under its guard—and ripped its

belly like an old sack." Gabriel had the air of a sports commentator at a boxing match after a knockout. Then he continued in a more ruminative mood, "Still it is a pity he didn't hold on a little longer. Even if tackling tigers is the toughest of problems—which I doubt—I'm still backing those hands of yours against all the paws, claws, fangs and tusks in the whole world."

The Pig overheard that. For by now he'd cleaned up, and was going off to receive the congratulations of his family. But he thought he deserved a few bows from the group who had witnessed his truly amazing counter-attack.

"We'll see!" he snuffed, "I'm not a brute nor a boaster. I don't want to eat my enemy—that's obvious. Simply the gentle art of self-defense. And as I said, before giving this brief demonstration of skill, it's really all skill, finesse, dash and point. Nothing clumsy about the whole thing. Quick as a flash, wasn't it, and as clean! Just because I'm the quickest, lithest thing on four feet, though you might never suspect it. Clumsiness—why, that's quite alien to my nature! I'm not disputing your angel friend's fancy that you should keep light, alive, springy, on your toes. All I'm saying is, that's precisely what I've done. And when you can rip up a tiger in the split second before he smashes your head in—well, I'll be the first to bow to you as my betters!"

He tossed his tusked head in the air and went off after his admiring family. "But he won't be able to stay lithe—that's the trouble about all that tusking," murmured Gabriel. "To be alive you must be lively and to be lively you must be small. Mark my words, that pig won't be able, for he won't really be content, to remain a dashing fellow like that. No, he'll begin to find that it's swell to swell—and how! And then he'll be done."

All this—which Gabriel kept on nagging into those of his little brood who were still ready to listen to him—was, of course, the most obvious common sense. For the most persistent temptation seems to be precisely that—to blow up, first mentally and then bodily. We tackle some exasperatingly fussy job—with a person or a thing or ourselves—a job which needs patience, insight, tact, precision— all those skills of hand and heart which come so hardly and are so difficult to hold—and, just when the thing—or person or self —should come round, fall in, click right—we do just what we don't want, we let the whole business fly to pieces. We leap up like boiling milk, blowing, blustering and making a fine mess and smell. Yes, our lot has gone on making that mistake for literally millions of years. We've seen it with the Whales in the sea and the Baluchitherium fifty million (maybe more) years ago. One might have hoped that—at the lateish part of our story, which our forebears had now reached—they'd have learned the sense of the slogan which Gabriel had been trumpeting in their ears from the start, "Size doesn't pay."

But the pig bunch, sad to say, had become pig-headed. Ahead, for them, was something to go head-on with. So they wanted more weight and, inevitably, bigger tusks. Gabriel was right. The Boar wasn't going to stay a light-weight, with dash and punch neatly balanced. Did you ever know of anyone who believed in armaments who thought theirs were big enough? So, first, as true pigs, we've seen they were much given to rooting and routing—which of course, is good for the snout and teeth—but not so good for the brain or the eyes. Naturally, you'd expect tusks to develop. Quite apart from the convenience of being able to duel with a self-grown bayonet always fixed ready for action in your mouth, it was a good idea surely to have a pick and shovel in your jaw? All of our lot had started with teeth that were fine little chisels and neat hammers. Why not, then, make them on a larger scale and then superscale? That could be done by becoming a whale of a pig—that's to say an elephant.[1]

However . . . the tusk invention kept on going wrong. And not for the lack of trying. One sort tried tusks coming out from the lower jaw. There's something to be said for that. You get under things better. But, if you push really hard, you push your jaw out of lock. Then another sort tried upper and lower at once—which obviously led to overlapping. At this dubious date it seems to have been decided that the Pig had been right in his original plan of attack—one should start out from the upper jaw. Certainly it had proved a success with the Boar and so it was gone ahead with. Indeed, one set of pigglings so seized upon the idea that you might say they got tusks on the brain. They grew into such unwieldly monsters that they've been called the Titanotheres—the Titan beasts. For they seem to have argued in their deep wish-minds, "If a thing's good, well then, you can't have too much of it." Since they found they could grow tusks from their teeth, tusks that would curl up round their lips, which let them stab and slit and root at anything they liked—it must have seemed an even cleverer thing to have ridges of such tusk-teeth right along the top of their nosing snouts.

Imagine—not only teeth inside your mouth to chew with, but fangs on the top of your mouth and nose to tear your way through things and persons—that was the Titan-notion. However, the pretty idea failed to foresee one thing—if you are to have a large row of spikes standing up and out of each side of your nose, what will happen to your eyes? You won't be able to see much, if anything. That's what seems to have happened to those experimental monster pigs—they just died out. And how fit they were—when they had blown themselves up to their full, silly, blind size—how fit they were for just dying out and nothing else, you can see for yourself when you look at the procession of them which Dr. Henry Fairfield Osborn arranged from actual fossils in the American Museum of Natural History, New York.

But, though growing lines of tusks in front of your eyes was evidently an extreme of foolishness and effectively put you out of the running, long sweeping tusks, much bigger than any Boar's, did seem to be a fashion that had come to stay and make its mark in the world. Perhaps the owners of these tusks thought they might even push their way right to the top, right on so as to become king of all the animals. But, like most successes they didn't seem able to stop from becoming excesses. Indeed, the tusks seemed (after a point) to be able to grow on their own almost—regardless of elephant economy. Unable to let a good thing alone, they almost appear as if they were out for themselves—as armies sometimes do, ceasing to remember they were grown and kept for the defense of the whole. Their aim seems to have been just to be the biggest ever. You'd think they thought they were the flower and the elephant simply the pot.

And so one day, our group was whisking and nibbling about when they all of a sudden became dead still. "Is that an earthquake?" said one whose ear was close to the ground. A large heavy head of barley that was hanging temptingly overhead nodded vigorously in confirmation. But Gabriel who was strolling around in the sky called out, "It's only a relation who is paying us a call in his new model—to show what he's purchased with the last of his wishes."

They looked about, expecting to see another bright idea in flesh-and-blood motor-bodies, which, if over-smart, at least would be striking and with no end of gadgets. But at first they saw nothing.

Then someone squealed, "There's a small hill moving down on us!" And they all scuttled up a tall stout tree.

True enough, a great mound was making its way toward them.[2] Obviously, too, it accounted for the earth tremors. But what on earth was it! Let alone who? The sloping heap was covered with what looked like a thick grass, dank and tangled, that hung down to the ground. As this wilted-looking hay swayed to and fro—under its rank herbage, they caught sight of a kind of matted rusty-red moss. And, at the foot of the mound, where the grass swung

most, every now and then the butt end of a big post thrust out
and pounded down on the earth. About two-thirds of the way
up the slope, on the side that was coming toward them, they saw
two great yellow shafts that stuck out and curved up into the air.
Then, suddenly, out of the heap swung a big snake, which
snatched at their tree, tore off quite a tidy branch, curled back
with this spoil—and a mouth opened—just below where the
serpent's body went into the hill—and into this gaping hole the
branch was thrust. There came a sound as though a hundred
people were all chewing celery in front of a battery of amplifying
microphones, and a rather fodder-confused voice said, "You won't
mind my browsing while I talk. We Mammoths, you know, have
won the Tusk-Prize, hands down, and we have to keep up our
position."

The group was so relieved that it wasn't a snake on a moving
mountain that they were quite willing to be accommodating.
"They certainly are some tusks," they agreed, running their eyes
up and down those sweeping curves, and their own tongues, a
little uneasily, round their own lips. It was almost impossible to
believe one's eyes—that teeth could ever have been made to grow

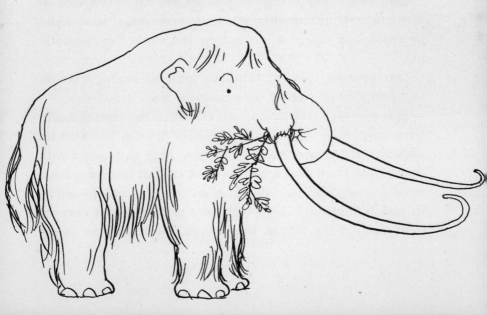

with so extravagant a flourish. They deserved that rather too often used word, *stupendous*. Of solid ivory and weighing about a quarter of a ton, they curled out and round like the moustachios which retired old colonels used to grow from their unspent residues of balked martial ardor. The mammoth lifted his trunk again, but this time with a flourish as courtly as a cavalier sweeping off his big plumed hat, and then through this elongated nose he let out a trumpeting that would have made a poor brass trumpet go still yellower, just out of envy. That made someone off in the forest nearby snarl. The mammoth squealed with insulted dignity. You'd have thought then he would have looked over his shoulder—for it was from that direction that the sour remark had come. But the mammoth seemed to have a stiff neck and had to prance round.

rather like a monstrous marionette, till he was facing[3] whence the sound had come—and a challenging smell in pungent wafts. Then, with amazing dash, he rushed headlong into the bush. But, after a frightful rumpus, he had to come out backwards—the least dignified of re-entries. His grand permanently-stiff-curled whiskers had got hopelessly caught and tangled in the trees.

"His hair *is* a bit on the romantic side," Gabriel allowed, as the small sleek ones watching from their tree sniggered at the hind view, which was even shaggier than the front, "but, as you no doubt are beginning to appreciate, in this kind of weather that your world seems lately to have run into, a thick coat is far better business than a smart one. And he certainly scores there, doesn't he?"

The audience, reminded of the mean temperature, gave a number of shivering, shuddering, wavering, but none the less very convincing nods. For the climate, as we are approaching our story's end—that is to say, within the last couple of millions of years of it—had now definitely begun to turn what gay common people call "nippy"—weather men, subzero—and geologists, Glacial. In fact, the Ice Age was now coming down. "No," continued Gabriel, "there's nothing wrong with his hair. There seldom's any harm in being a little over-hirsute. It's nails and teeth that get one into trouble. And it will be that way with him, if I'm not mistaken. What he'll have to do is to stop that kind of permanent wave of his teeth, that superivory curl." The Archangel smiled. "Naturally, he's rather proud of it, but it's getting utterly out of hand—so much so that I'm wondering whether he can now stop it."

As usual, the AA was right. For, as time went on, not so long after the Mammoths succeeded in being the growers of the world's biggest whiskers, they themselves died out.

The Tusks That Took Over

But the mammoths had some descendants—or perhaps they were not direct descendants, perhaps they were more like nephews or second cousins once, twice and three times removed—as genealogists say—and these later relatives did begin to see that all this untamed tusk-growing was tending to push the whole lot of them—as tree-climbers say—out onto the end of a limb. The Elephants which we have today seem to be descendants of some cousin of those over-toothed mammoths, a cousin who had begun to think that it was possible to raise and rear too much self-grown ivory. As we all know, at least one group of the present-day Elephants, the one which comes from India, is far from being a fool. All the time that the tusk temptation has been tugging at this lot they have been trying to balance that pull toward tough-ness and pure push, by somehow keeping on being inquiring and sensitive. But what were they to do? They had let go their hands, those question-raising things with finders, pointers and feelers, the fingers. They had shut them up in barrels of muscle, and then stood on them—almost like the Baluchitherium.

Look at an elephant's front foot. True, he has five nails as our hands have. But the whole thing ends in being even a blunter end of a pillar than is the leg of a grand piano. There's no use complaining. It just has to be that way—if you insist on weighing tons. Still the Elephant is very intelligent—a quiet, reflective person—who has been known to think over things for years with that big brain of his. Being a vegetarian, too, he doesn't have to go rushing and roaring, raging and tearing, every time he wants a meal. And it certainly seems that he has thought up an ingenious, if not a final, answer to the problem: if your hand has turned into a foot and a tusk has no tact, how is one to keep from losing all real touch with things? If you can't any longer put out a hand, what can you do? If you have enough time and will, you can put out your nose—if it still remains soft, inquiring, curious. Of course, that was the old original answer made by almost every animal when we all came out of the sea and began to get the wind of things. Scent was our first guide and "follow your nose" was the best advice. But by mid-mammal time we've seen noses had been tending already for quite a while to hand over the problem to hands. Yet, by putting his really quite big brain behind it, the Elephant succeeded in making quite a wonderful compromise. Noses are, of course, for smell and when we smell we naturally shut our eyes and say either, "How delicious" or "Please open the window and call for the plumber."

The Elephant, however, knew what he was about, considering how he had misplaced himself. And considering that, considering that he couldn't go back, grow small again, get up on his hind legs and recover his fingers, his trunk line experiment, though a side line and in the end getting nowhere, was the only way of keeping going even for a while. As you know, the trunk not only went on growing longer and longer till he had a nose the length of what his arm should have been and with which he could brush the floor when he wished. But he did even better. He showed final insight, when at the end of this arm-nose of his—which he grew to a finer tip than even the most aristocratic grand duchess has ever turned up at our snubbier ones—at the end of this apparatus he grew a delicate flap[1] In fact, the African Elephant, which isn't as brainy as the Indian, has grown two such flaps to act like our thumb and fingertips. Next time in the zoo, if you haven't made an elephant's acquaintance yet, feel that odd finger's touch as it solicits like a well-trained beggar, a biscuit from your hand. It is softer than most people's fingers and almost as skillful. Its minor accomplishments—such as being able to shower bath yourself all over your broad back from your nose, to being able to pick a dime off the floor—are miracles of co-ordination quite apart from its strength. If you were an Elephant you could put a teak beam on your tusks and so carry it with tusks and trunk in play together, or pick up your master and land him neatly on your head, or snatch a Tiger from your neck and fling him on the ground— with your delicate thumb-and-fingered elongated arm of a nose.

But surely this ability suggests that the Elephant doesn't, in his deep racial mind, feel that being tough and big is the answer to everything. We put our finger to our nose to show contempt. He's turned his nose into a finger, to show what? Could it be humility? Is he signaling for help? Does he want to come back to us again? But how is he to get back? No one knows that yet. The poor fellow's size does pose a problem very hard to solve. We do know that now nearly all the other kinds of Elephants are gone. The two that survive are considerably smaller than some that used to be. Perhaps our circus friend will be able to get down again from the massive stilts on which he has climbed and so will crawl back to safety-size again. That is his only chance. Once he was useful as a tractor. He, the biggest of all the land mammals, because he was mild could be used to pull big weights. But now, with our ingenious minds we have made tractors stronger than he and much less difficult to feed—besides they're not given to temperament, which he sometimes is.

What is to be done with all his mountain of muscle? It is worth noting though, that having blown up to this huge size he seems to have become mild. He has a small liver and no gall bladder. So, even physically, he may have become uninclined to have outbursts. The settled conviction that one must make one's weight tell—well, it has told. The Elephant is so big that he has no one to fear, save the little animal with the bigger brain and the fine-fringed front paw—ourselves. He is also wise enough to fear a fall. He realizes that when you have grown as big as he has, though no one may be able to slap you down, one slip and your own weight may break you. Even cross elephants can be kept quiet if you can clap hold of one of their feet. They live in mortal dread of being tripped and thrown. Indeed, he now seems to suffer unduly from fears and shrink from what appear to us imaginary risks. He has been known to show as much panic as a Victorian spinster when a mouse ran into his stall. His fear is said to be due to dread that it might attack his Achilles' heel—it might think his nostril to be a city of refuge and with a mouse settled in his trunk he would not know what to do—he would be as much embarrassed as we would be with a cockroach in our throat. It would seem that, having gotten over his inner wish to burst up—having blown himself to the full—there's nothing more for him to do. There can't be a doubt, he's a mistake. And sometimes looking into that small sad eye as it solicits a bun, one feels that he knows it and that he is begging for something even more costly than his keep. He is begging for—escape perhaps—escape from the captivity of his vast skin—a way out.

So the Mammoth pomped and pounded off . . . Every now and then when he got into a forest having to stop his stately swing to get his made-in-solid-ivory whiskers out of some tree in which they had caught. One of our group squeaked up at Gabriel, "Somehow he seems to have a stiff neck."

Gabriel smiled back. "Here, come for a ride," and sweeping down, balanced the whole remaining brood of those-yet-to-have-their-wish along the edge of one of his glowing wings. "Here's where he'll end. At least till I call you all in the final morning," said the Archangel as the flight ended in a dell. It was full of huge bones. "They like coming to rest at the same spot and bones of that size last, so you have a tidy collection here." The great skeletons rested rather like big abandoned trailers.

"It certainly took some muscle to heave all this," said one of our lot as he extemporized a neat piece of gymnastic work, using for parallel bars the late departed's front teeth.

"That's it," remarked Gabriel, "in fact, that's what I wanted you to see—those tusks alone took a mass of special tackling. Now look at the back of his head."

"Why, it's as flat as though some other Mammoth had leaned against it when it was soft," chuckled one of the inspecting party.

"That's why he had to turn the whole of himself around, couldn't turn his neck, when he heard and scented the tiger," Gabriel was quite enjoying himself as a lecturer in vertebrate anatomy. "That big flat back to his skull is simply to give grip for the very big neck muscles. You've just got to have a neck as thick as the trunk of a tree if you insist on growing full-sized branches of solid ivory out of your mouth. And when you have a neck of that thickness of course it can't be bent."

"Oh," shouted someone. His voice boomed oddly and when they looked for him they couldn't see him—till he hopped out from under the huge skull. "It's just like a beehive inside, it's nothing but a mass of cells—you might have blown it with bubbles!"

"He just had to grow like that," explained Gabriel. "He had to have a huge skull for those tusk-wielding muscles to get a grip on, but the skull bone itself, though it must be large, must also be light. If it weighed what it looks like it should, why then just carrying it would be too much and we'd never get round to the problem of those very demanding tusks. Your poor mistaken, mistaking, mischoosing fellows do set problems for the small grain of creative capacity given to all of you, and locked up inside you, to be used when you really have decided what you wish to be! How wonderfully the magic power strives to make their silly wishes work at all and not prove fatal to the foolish wisher! And yet in the end—in spite of all this skill of the inventive power within—the foolish wish proves a fatal handicap. Do you see?" He asked with something almost of urgency, which is as far as an Archangel can go toward anxiety, "Do you think that any of you will see?"

The Small Sore One
OR
Being Small Isn't All

The little group was getting just a little bored. Bones and theories don't really make a very good attention-holding mixture. They began to scatter and Gabriel who, of course, is nearly as patient as the Creator was just about to float up to his native element—as you let yourself rise when you've done a rather long underwater swim—when one of the group who was always scratching his head and so setting up all sorts of questions in the brain inside (or the other way round—it probably doesn't really matter) suddenly called up to where the soles of the archangelic feet hung in the high blue like a last wisp of sunset cloud, "Gabriel!"

"Yes, Scratch-Scalp!" came down a voice very high and distant but clear as the cry you can hear Swans make when they fly at evening vastly far up, going north to their nesting places.

"Gabriel, the one thing we must never do is to blow up—is that it?"

"Well, that's certainly half the truth."

"You mean that just bottling in isn't enough?"

"Don't you think that must be so? Surely, if you really want to blast everything to thunder, and just don't—you must know it's something really very deep down in you that 'turns your wishes into seams, laces and stitches' as the old rhyme says. Don't you suppose that 'it' knows what you'd really like to do and be? Perhaps you don't become an unwieldy monster. Maybe it'd be better if you did. Whales and Elephants, maybe they're at a dead end, but they seem to know it, don't they?"

"They seem," answered Scratch-Scalp, "now one comes to think of it, to be, how shall I put it—?"

"Resigned?" suggested Gabriel.

"That's it," said the ruminating one, pleased with the word. "Resigned—that means they've given up the game."

"Thrown in their hand," added Gabriel. "But do you remember that Small Whale that ate out the Big Whale's tongue? Don't you think he might have been better off, if, having become a whale, he'd just gone the whole whale way, instead of sinking all his pent energy into just becoming a Shark? Anyhow, look at this."

By this time the group, scenting Gabriel might have another show up his sleeve, had gathered again "What is it?"

"I think it makes the matter clear up to date."

"How?" asked all the group as their attention was directed rather disappointingly to a largish dock-leaf.

Gabriel raised it slightly and out ran what looked like a small Mouse with very small eyes almost hidden in its fur and a very sharp nose that seemed bent to get into other people's business. "The smallest of you all," Gabriel remarked.

"There's no need to make personal remarks," a voice like a needle darted out. "I might just as well remark that you are distinctly overgrown. And, though I've not had time and am not lazy enough to sit about being lectured, I thought when I was going about my business that I'd heard some talk about keeping small and ship-shape!"

Gabriel being one of the first courtiers in all creation and therefore very courteous and having also a voice capable of more modulations than any other in the whole universe, changed his tone so that his original audience could hear but the newcomer need

not be ruffled. "He's smaller," Gabriel went on in this safety whisper, "than even the first form you had when, at the beginning of these conversations, you decided to vote for hair and warm blood and to look after your young. But if you'll observe, he's not been left unprotected! My Master, your Father . . ." and Gabriel burst out laughing like sunshine—it was one of his super-laughs. "O Glory," he shouted, "how wonderful Creation is!" And then the joyful roar swelled to supersonic intensity which fortunately for their ears they couldn't hear. "O Glorious," he cried, "how inconceivable Thou art. Nothing is lacking, not even humor." And then turning back to the group he questioned, "Do you notice anything?"

So encouraged, a few who were nearest the newcomer edged away and turning politely aside, whispered, "Now you ask, there is rather—well, the kind of smell that makes one feel that it would be wiser to miss a meal. I mean it suggests that someone has just been quite unmistakably sick."

Gabriel chuckled, "Would you believe it, that's his defense.[1] And it's perfectly good. Not one of the prowlers will touch such a super-sour smelling person. Only the Owl, which can't smell, can endure to touch him. It's a wonderful defense." Again Gabriel chuckled. "And," he added, giving a low strange whistle, "here's another body who has proved quite content with it." The soured air began to be chemically cleaned with a strong ammonia smell. Like a Dog coming to its master's whistle, a Skunk ambled out. "Does anyone molest you?" Gabriel asked, and the creature looked up at the angel face now luminous but undazzling as the full moon.

"None," said the Skunk, "since I was given this fragrant tip to my tail. I just offer my snuff to an intruder. He never wants another pinch."

Angel and Skunk grinned at each other, the Skunk ambled off.

"It's not the best he could have done with his wish-power," Gabriel went on after a polite pause. "But it's quite a good second best. But we have another friend here— quite a cheesy chap who really has no grounds for complaint. But see if that's made him content."

Then, pulling out another stop in the great organ of his voice, he became audible once more to the small one sitting by the dock-leaf. "How are you feeling today? In plenty of spirits, Mr. Shrew?" for that was his name and a shrewd one.

"I hope I have," hissed the Shrew. "And whether or not Heaven knows, I know I need to be. And while you're lounging about with your great wings on the air, what I want to know is—why the hell do I have to be like this? The smallest mammal! Oh yes, I know what you've been politely advertising—a nice record to be held by a creature of spirit. If I'd my way I'd teach you all a lesson." He flashed a venemous look round the group which, not being martial, began to give him a little more room. "I must say," and the Shrew's voice was perfectly suited to his name, "that all of you seem to have a very offensive odor." His long nose curled and twisted with disgust. Someone tittered. The Shrew flashed into rage.

But providentially at that moment he caught sight of another of his own kind. Simultaneously, without a moment's delay, they remarked to each other, "What do you think you're doing here!" and without further waste of time went for each other's throats.

The mix-up was so complete, each was such "a creature of spirit" that you couldn't tell their bodies apart until it was over, with one (or the other, again the group couldn't tell) not only getting killed but actually eaten up to the last whisker by his rapacious foe.

"He doesn't like such a diet," remarked Gabriel, "for he's still by all his animal tastes just as you were at the start—an insect eater—with some beech nuts thrown in now and then. But you see, being a person of spirit, what is one to do, when victory has been won? It is necessary to show one is not to be played with. The enemy might stage a comeback. No, when one beats a foe, it is best to eat him—then the matter is ended till one meets another foe—and again it's *beat or be beaten* . . . *eat or be eaten* . . .

"But he looks a very sensitive, alive person," remarked one of our group.

"Yes," allowed Gabriel, "he's sensitive in a way, in a hell of a way. Everything seems to outrage him. He's really in an incessant passion."

"But what about?"

"Seems that he's just sore because he's so small and harmless."

"You mean all the unspent energy in him has gone—gone sour as it were."

"Guess you may be right," said Gabriel. "If you stoke like that, the energy's got to go somewhere." They glanced after their aggressive visitor who had scuttled off. At every step he pounced on some small worm or beetle and gulped it down. "He never stops voracing and devouring like that," mused Gabriel.

"So," Scratch-Scalp questioned, "so he's still all thwarted inside? He hasn't solved his problem by just looking small when all the time actually he's boiling to bursting with his wish to be big? Is that it? Have we got to do with our inside selves something as big as the Elephant and Whale have done with their outside selves?"

Scalp-Scratch scratched and itched at himself all over as though a cargo of fleas had made a landing on him, then looked up at Gabriel who remained a great question mark and scratched pensively again. "Somehow," he said at last, "somehow that question seems to have been biting me for quite a while."

"Well really," said Gabriel, "that's all I really wanted to know. Perhaps the time to answer it hasn't really come," and then finding that he'd said "really" three times, he remarked, "Really, I mustn't be hanging about, there's plenty to do. I'll be getting behind with my announcements. Three Novae to be noticed, not to speak of a fine crop of sunspots nearer this base. But," and he looked back over his spread wing while raising his great sky-spanning trumpet to his incandescent lips, "I really do believe that one day one of you is going to answer that question and that answer may explain everything."

The One Who Thought the Way
Was Underground

The group hardly noticed what Gabriel was saying or even that he had gone. For at that moment the earth began to stir under their feet and, like most of us, their feelings affected them more than their views: seeing, they often remarked to one another, may be believing, but feeling is knowing. And there was a queer feel under their paws—the earth wasn't trembling but, as you might say, it was crawling or crumbling. Then, after a moment, a rather snuffling voice came up out of the heaping soil they were watching.

"You think you've seen all the ways out, don't you? The sea-way and become a fool of a fish; the plain-way and become a run-away; the air-way and flop about breathlessly chasing insects. Never seems to have occurred to any of you that there's another way, the right-way—you're all so sharp and quick that you've overlooked that!"

"Where?" asked someone, as much to locate the mysterious speaker as to hear of his discovery, "where?"

"Why, underground of course!"

The mound that had been growing in front of their noses at

that point gave an extra heave and out of its side stuck a very black object at the tip of which was a pale white nose. "What?" asked the mouth under the nose, "what does anyone want but food, protection and comfort?" And having made that statement with some emphasis the mouth closed, while the nose turned from side to side, as though testing public opinion. For no eyes seemed visible in the head which, save for nose and mouth, appeared to be covered with black velvet.[1]

"It must be pretty dirty, living in the soil like that!" remarked someone more interested in practical detail than in sweeping generalizations.

"Observe my coat," said their visitor in a voice whose sharpness made up for the coat's softness, "I would be amused if any of you sissies who are afraid of a steady day's digging and mining could show a pelt as unsoiled as mine. I'm rightly called The Little Gentleman in Black Velvet. My coat is so fine that never any earth gets into it, though I'm not afraid of hard work or getting my hands right into the good soil." He stuck himself out a little further from his small self-made hill and showed a couple of large, ugly paws, pasty-colored but muscular and shod with great clawlike nails.

"But how do you see? Your fur coat seems to have grown itself right over your eyes?" asked someone who had been peering at the soot-black fellow.

"Don't need 'em!"

"But you've no ears worth speaking of either!"

"I don't need to be echo-sounding either, I can see all I need—and that's to know when it's wise to go under—and it's under that the larder lies! I know! My nose is what I need. All that looks luscious often isn't, you know that, but all that smells is—and that's that. That poor little cousin of mine, that shrew, well I was like him once. But I saw the right way. I don't need to stink as he has to, because I can smell out my dinner and dig myself in safe from enemies, all by one maneuver." And he stuck out again his long nose with not a little contempt at his audience.

"Your arm's all cramped," snapped back one of them, both pleased to give tit for tat and all the more ready to do so, seeing that the intruder from underneath obviously had for some reason no reach at all. His paw and claws were ugly enough and they waved about rather like the whale's side fins.

"Why you couldn't even point at a thing!" said another, pointing rather rudely.

"Don't need to!" said the digger dourly. "My hand is for work and my arm works all the better through my making the neat invention of tucking up my forearm against my upper arm and putting them both neatly folded under my skin. It's what's called streamlining. I may be strong, I am, but I'm also deft and I fit myself to my job. I fit exactly the passage I dig which is both my home—and a very safe one—and my hunting ground, and a very rich one."

"But what happens if you meet someone in the same burrow? There's no room to pass if you fit your tunnel so neatly?"

The Mole—for that, of course, was what this black underground person had made himself with his wish—the mole smiled. It wasn't a pleasant grin, but certainly it was amply informative. For there flashed out a row of teeth which, considering their scale, were not unworthy of a tiger. "True enough," he remarked complacently, "true enough, there's not room to pass. But then, though the worms at the right underground level are plentiful, there's no reason why they should be thinned out by a poacher and trespasser that wished to use the tunnel I've dug with my muscles! So when I come up against an intruder, well," and he chuckled, "well, I just go on my way, I just go on eating, I eat my way right through him!" and he smacked his traplike jaws. "Well, I must be

getting on. That silly glare you call sunlight is poking into this
hollow where we've met. Besides a person of health and energy
like me is hungry most of the time. Dig and eat, and eat and dig,
that's my motto, that's my rhythm and a fine one. And mark me,
my little hoppers and flitters, we Moles have spread nearly all
over the earth. There's hardly one of your lot who has gone so far
afield as we and explored so widely so many countries! That proves
the Underground's the Right Way. Why all the world can't be
like my galleries—neither too hot in summer nor too cold in
winter! You see, the perfectly balanced place! I've found it and
it's a couple of feet down. Why? Well, I suppose no one knows
but the Master Mole that molded everything!"

The great ugly white paws with their spikelike nails began to
tear into the soil. Hardly a moment after two little kicking hind
feet and an absurd scut of a tail alone were visible squirming above
ground; an instant more and they were gone too, having followed
the blind black face into the earth.

"The silly glare," however, wasn't the dawn. It was Gabriel
having called back, after his christening cruise round part of the
galaxy, to wish the group good night.

"He's going down, too?" asked Scratch-Scalp, pointing to the
little heap of earth down which like an earthy tear every now and

then trickled a few crumbs of soil as the self-buried mole underneath dug himself deeper.

"He's done pretty well for himself, hasn't he?" cross-questioned Gabriel. "Safer off than the Shrew and sweeter too—at least as far as smell is concerned. And he's solved food, housing and defense! Aren't those the only three 'Musts'?"

"But what about his eyes?"

"Ah!" said the Archangel, and his own great orbs got such a faraway look that he himself began to vanish from the group's sight. "I expect that *would* be worth looking into—I expect if you went on looking in that direction—I expect—" and he was gone.

The Fool Who Put Horns on His Nose

But the group didn't continue looking after their friend. They were sleepy anyhow. And next morning, when Scratch-Scalp began to ask, "What do you think he meant? I mean in what direction? I mean where are we to keep on looking?"

"Quiet!" they squeaked, "Keep your mouth shut." For once again the earth began to tremble, really tremble, a real infectious shudder.

"Another Mammoth!" After the first awkward silence this was the rallying contribution of those of the party who were to grow —after a million more years or so—into that type of person, who, after having been once surprised, is determined not to be caught out again or made wide-awakedly uneasy. So they always hasten to inform us that anything that looms up now is really only what happened last time. The new thing, which certainly shook the earth in much the same way, and nearly as much, as the Mammoth, did somehow give the impression of being both very old and at the same time very odd, what might be called in cut and style a striking departure. We generally count a person's age by the number and depth of wrinkles he has. On that count this person looked a millionaire in years. The Elephant had been fairly creased and baggy, as we say of suits that are far more comfortable than smart.

But this newcomer looked as though he'd wrapped himself in layers of leather mats. The grooves between them—for it is really impossible to get a neat fit if your suit is semi-rigid—were being examined carefully by birds that ran up and down his back, and out of these deep grooves—it's hardly nice but certainly true—these birds were pulling out all sorts of boring insects who were making this armor-skinned monster most uncomfortable but about which he could do no more, in spite of all his strength, than a new-laid egg can do if a blue-bottle sits on it.

That might have accounted partly for his temper which was short and his tone which was gruffly arrogant. "Thought I heard you talking about what could be done with hair."

"Yours seems to have gone," perked up one of our more well-groomed members of the group.

"As usual, with the small and oversmart," sneered back old Leather-Mats. "Failure to observe makes for mendacity. You were talking to those pompous Elephants and that absurd little bore of a Boar. Now, as a matter of fact I'm the perfect balance between those two." Someone tittered. But being certain of his case, the visitor didn't get too angry. "Indeed, I may tell you, as a not uninteresting autobiographic fact, that when I was building myself up to my present balance of force and finish of form, I once tried out that boar invention—if it really deserves the name. As a matter of fact, today I have a rather weak and backward cousin[1] who still goes with his tusks at anyone who insults him. I saw that was clumsy . . ." Again someone in the audience gave way to an audible smile. But Leather-Mats felt so sure the laugh would be on his side as soon as he made his point that he sailed on. "I thought up

a completely original weapon made by a completely new method."
He swung round, pointing with the one thing that was pointed
about him, his nose. "Look at that Tiger."

They looked. Tigers are fairly quick with their paws but pretty
unnimble with their brains. So this Tiger that Leather-Mats pointed
at contemptuously was now only offending the nose, not making
your heart beat with fear. He was just one more of the long line
of tigers that—as we've seen—ran into living bacon and instead
of getting their stomach full of rashers got their stomach ripped
and emptied from stem to stern. It certainly was not a nice
sight and wasn't getting nicer. "Well," said Leather-Mats, "I can
do that with an elephant, if I wish." The Rhino (for of course
it was he) tossed his horn-tipped snout in the air. "And," he continued, "here's the joke of it, my sleek and silky little friends,
this horn of mine, that would split a tree, is made, guess of what?[2]

Of the very thing that you use to wrap yourselves up with, soft and cozy. Hair didn't make a sissy of me. I've turned my tresses into a battle-axe. That's an amusing tour de force, isn't it!" And he gave a cough of a laugh. "No tooth trouble for me. Simply bring my moustache to a fine point, and—"

At that moment the cat smell came again. With amazing agility the ton or more of muscle, bound round with leather matting, went into top gear—and didn't the earth shake. Down went the Rhino's head with his horn level as a charging bayonet. But as his head was down he, of course, couldn't see where he was going. Faced with a foe twice his size and obviously in full armor the giant cat wisely streaked off to the left. Like an engine whose driver is dead, the bucketing mound of fury crashed on. Unfortunately for him the ground some distance in front fell suddenly into a dry river bed. Over the edge he went. Even if he could then have seen, it would have been too late for him to stop himself.

The group scuttled after. He was lying at the bottom as dead as the Tiger whom the Boar had opened.

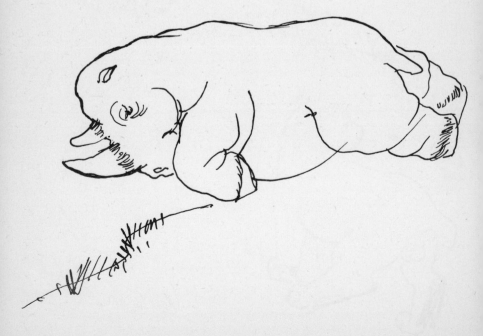

"I guess," said Scratch-Scalp to a fellow woolgatherer, "I guess, if you weigh all that, nothing can stand up to you, but if they move away and won't act obligingly as a buffer, then of course, you are apt to knock yourself out."

"Yet if you have made the tip of the curl on the end of your nose your main weapon, how are you to use it without putting your head down? And then you can't see?" the other replied.

"Well, he certainly was an odd one," they concluded.

"But," said Gabriel's voice who had apparently been looking on at this shadow-boxing and self-knockout, "the Rhino was once one of you. He's just another example of how you can get your wish. You can make a weapon out of any part of you if you really want to. Bees, wasps and hornets

have made it out of the little duct through which they used to lay their eggs. Rhino's bright idea to make a pickax out of his hair was really brilliantly silly. But after all it's only one more way of going wrong, just because he and all the others hadn't the patience to stay sensitive and thought they must be tough."

The Cat That Was Caught by the Claws
in Its Mouth

Still it's amazing how infectious a bad example can be. Even when it's clearly stupid; if it's spectacular, like too big tusks or too big ships or tanks, no end of people who call themselves realists simply fall for it. The Tiger who was still pretty lithe and limber and on the lookout so that he was able to streak off, avoid the Rhino and let old Leather-Mats crash himself—it's hard to believe that this Cat-leopard was more impressed by the Rhino's horn than he was amused by the lack of brain or even of foresight back of the horn. It took him, from first to last, some ten million years to prove himself to be such a super-fool—but in the end, in fact just in that last couple of million years we have come to in our story, this cat did it.

"Heavens," remarked Gabriel one day when he was floating over the top of a big tree in which our group was taking a siesta, "heavens! what terrible power has the All Powerful tied up inside you!"

"What's up?" said a couple stirring themselves, for they felt, not having his divine vitality, that Gabriel was apt to take an in-

tense interest in almost anything, and that sometimes proved difficult to keep up with.

But when he said, "Look," and their eyes followed his, theirs goggled with fear. For under
the tree stood a thing with tusks. But it was a
Tusked Tiger.[1]

"What a horror!" whimpered someone, scrambling higher up
the trunk.

"A horror, yes," Gabriel reassured them, "but I guess he's really more helpless than the Rhino. What startled me is not that he's such a fool. Our Master often tells us, His attendants, we have no idea how stupid self-will can make creatures. What beats me is that after millions of years stupefying himself by being a blood-sucking, flesh-tearing parasite on his fellows, he still had locked up in him a sufficient remnant of the divine inventing power to grow himself these insane sabers out of his mouth!"

"These are the biggest true-cutting teeth ever grown," snarled up the Sabre-toothed Tiger.

"Yes, and to grow them you've become a silly cripple," smiled back Gabriel. "You couldn't climb this tree as once your lot could. You couldn't touch one of this humble-footed and handy-pawed crew."

The crew aloft began to feel gay, superior, even interested under the double reassurance that they could look after themselves even if the boastful beast was near them—and of the even more satisfying information that he had lost the power to climb.

"I don't want to eat mice," snarled back the sabre-mouthed one, "and I don't need to climb trees."

"I guess," reckoned Gabriel who can tell the age of a species or a genus just as a vet does a horse by a glance at its teeth, "I guess it's taken you half a dozen million years to grow that toothy grimace. And what beats me is the sheer amount of ingenuity you've been allowed to have in order to make yourself such a laughing stock."

The beast roared with stupid rage and so doing opened its mouth. They all saw what insanely ingenious self-crippling had gone on. The lower teeth had had to be displaced. The degenerate brute could no longer take a decent healthy bite of anything. And most amazing, in order to accommodate these daggers in his mouth, he had to let drop his lower jaw like a drooling idiot does—for the silly sabres would catch in everything—and the lower jaw had to grow extensions to act as kind of sheath-grooves for those insanely big teeth—teeth so long that even when his mouth was wide open they nearly barred it.

"He's really as tooth-trapped as the Mammoth," joined in Scratch-Scalp, feeling quite content with his inoffensive fangs.

"Worse," remarked Gabriel and swooping more swiftly than a hawk—as his sight was so far better than the best bird's—he flashed off for a moment and was back as quickly. "I saw this lying about," he explained. "Here's another skull, pretty small you see, but it's a better forecast of what awaits that fanged-fool down there," and he whisked out a wing-tip down to where the Sabre-toothed Tiger was whetting his knives on the grass, "than any Elephant's head." In his big glowing palm lay a white thing small as a Hen's egg. "The skull of a small rabbit, you see, and you see how it died." "Why," one of the group was able to reply, "one of its lower teeth was knocked out and one of the uppers has gone on growing till it went right down across its mouth. It must have grown its tooth right into its throat."

"Before that it starved to death," Gabriel abbreviated the story. "And that's simply a quick motion picture of what now will befall the fanged-fool."

The owner (or the base) of the fangs, snarled again. Then the snarl suddenly rose to a kind of scream, a megaphoned multiplication of the mew a cat gives when it suspects you may have milk for it. But it wasn't milk this monster smelled.

They all caught a terribly strong stable-smell; then they heard a noise as though the Mammoth was coming back. It wasn't he, but something almost as broad and perhaps half as high—without tusks or trunk but with a proper nose that seemed to have trunk tendencies, without the drive to go full steam ahead, but with teeth that had pushed over the edge of the big lips and now didn't seem to know where to go. The floppy nose drooped over this mouth that was as loose as a ripped-open bag and from this bag, bits of food that had almost been swallowed kept on making last minute escapes. In fact, it was a giant, untidy early relation of that still not very shapely beast, the Tapir.

This one was larger and clumsier than the present-day Hippopotamous. He seemed to be too stupid to know that he'd come into company. He stumbled down the glade, his stumpy feet prodding into the earth and coming out again with a sucking sound that made a close imitation of the gurgling and champing his mouth was making. The Sabre-toothed Tiger gave a queer flick with its hind legs, flung back its head till its scalp was flat on its shoulders and its half-closed eyes could have seen its tail, bounded into the air and coming down struck—just as a rattler strikes with its long fangs—right into the flank of the dull waddler. And there it hung just like a leech. The victim mooed and tried to shake itself free of this animal burr and then, finding it couldn't, staggered off down the glade with its parasite nailed into it.

"Double stupidity must end in double death," remarked Gabriel. "You see, he'll kill off all those big clumsy fellows, clumsy enough to be caught and big enough to be speared in that way. And then he'll die out—he'll have starved himself out. And even if they, the stupid waddling roasts-of-beef didn't die out, he would have to go. For his teeth have seized the bit—they are growing on their own and to please themselves. The wish-power has got loose. He wished for teeth and now the teeth are going to have the last word —and that last word is what they have meant for the creatures round them and now will mean for the creature that grew them, for their owner—Death."

"It's very dangerous to get one's wish then?" Scratch-Scalp asked.

"Oh, I don't know I'd go as far as that," replied the Archangel, almost a trifle archly. "Or perhaps I ought to ask back—*who gets the wish?*"

"I don't get you," said Scratch-Scalp, giving his head a violent massage.

"Well, when you say you want your wish, *do you know who is you?*"

Scratch-Scalp felt so dizzy he thought he'd fall out of the tree —all the others, of course, had scampered off to amuse themselves long ago.

"Don't you see?" Gabriel knew this was a difficult point to get clear, "don't you see, it was the teeth and not the Tiger who really got the wish to be the fangiest-fanged beast that ever lived?"

"Oh, I see," crowed Scratch-Scalp, "he actually became what he wished, he became a fang and the fang has actually started eating him up!"

"Yes, he's now nothing but a root out of which that parasite tooth is growing and swelling. And do you know, just as a flying lizard actually did what the poor little bat has done now—only scores of millions of years later and no better—so, too, with this silly criminal fang business. Between the lizards and your selves there was (and there are still a few of) another halfway lot. They have warm blood, but they haven't your way of tending their young, and so, for fear they would forget them and leave them

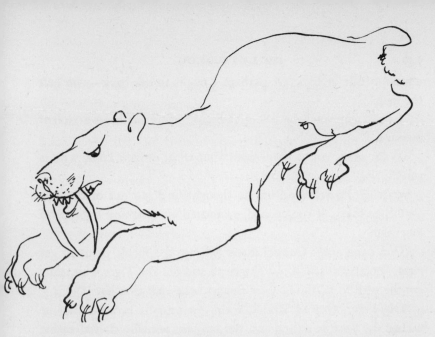

about as the lizards do—they were let think up the clever idea for people too stupid to remember—a large pocket in which you can put your valuables and forget about them. They are the pouched animals, the marsupials, and strange as it may seem, they have made every one of the mis-wishings and mistakes which your lot have now made—even to this grotesque fang-blunder.[2] Yes, there was a pouched, warm-blooded marsupial who became a Sabre-toothed Tiger and he was able to beat that silly fellow that we saw go off gaffed onto the even stupider fellow who let him make a landing. For the Sabred beast you've been watching was once one of you—and once had a promising brain. And the hump made by that stood in the way of those parasite teeth sending their roots any further than up the sides of his cheeks. But with the marsupial, as I've told you, his brain was smaller and so didn't hump so much and so didn't stand in the way of the teeth thrusting their roots as far into their carrier as he thrust their points into his prey. And the roots proved as fatal to the monster as the points were fatal to his victims. The roots drove their way right across the top of his skull until his brain, small to start with, was barred down and became in fact little more than a seed plot for the tooth-roots."

The thought made Scratch-Scalp's head itchier than ever. "If I wish something for myself, for my body, and then some part of my body steals the gift and so gets the power to grow till I'm its victim—why, what then? There's a double question: I've got to ask, haven't I, not only *what* am I to wish—but—*for whom* am I to wish?"

"Now you've said a mouthful," answered Gabriel.

"But I really want to know the answer!"

"Oh, then I expect you will. That's the kind of want and wish that does somehow get answered." Gabriel was really very pleased, indeed almost excited—or as archangels prefer to say, exultant—but he thought it better not to show it. So he closed, as he sailed off into the sky. "However, I think we can agree that if you wish tusks or teeth, *they* and not *you* will get the last word."

He Who Got His Finger Stuck In The Pie

Then, thinking that Scratch-Scalp had already used his coming-on brain quite enough, indeed, so much he might be in danger not only of leaving all the rest of the group behind, but of coming-in-two himself, his mind going on and his body getting left behind—and that would never do—Gabriel's voice boomed back with a favorite slogan of his, "Keep up the Five-Finger Exercises!"

"Aye, aye."

Everyone looked round to see who had seconded the motion—none of them had—indeed, they were more than a little tired of the admonition and thought that silence gave sufficient consent to this constant counsel.

"Aye, aye," said the small squeaking voice again. It seemed to come from a fork in a tree near by. A further glance showed, draped along the branch, something that looked like a rather tired piece of fur, a small fur stole that the Moths might have found out.

They all turned to watch it. The fur uncurled a bit more and there protruded a small face rather like a withered puppy—if you can imagine such a thing—large, sad, lashless eyes and big nervous ears.

"Aye, aye," the creature said for the third time and added,

"Well, Your Highness, I've acted up to your advice, *I've* taken it to heart."

"All right," said Gabriel, but evidently not with any special enthusiasm toward this applicant for congratulation. "All right, show them what you've done."

"I'm a member," remarked the little croaking voice, "of one of the most interesting groups of all the mammals. I'm a Lemur—a very remarkable family. You'd think that some of us were Squirrels and others you'd say were the cutest of Dogs. We have beautiful coats," he paused a moment and combed his certainly not very tidy pelt. "And," he continued, "lovely large eyes. Some of us have long thick-furred tails of banded colors. But we're not Dogs nor Cats nor are we Squirrels—nor—" and the thing grimaced and hunched its back a little, "nor are we Monkeys, Apes or Sloths— or foolish fellows who can't make up their minds! We, I maintain, are beautifully balanced creatures—snout and hand, nose and fingers neatly balanced. You Monkey-ape lot have gone a bit too far."

"Excuse me," interrupted Gabriel, "are you talking about the whole of your rather large family or are you going to tell us about yourself? Your particular superiority?"

"I was coming to that," said the creature a little snappishly, "I should have thought you could have spared five minutes to take in some fifty million years of background. And I may tell you if you have any real interest in pure knowledge that I'm a sub-family all on my own." He said this with the air that those odd people who at great expense, have extinct titles dug up and revived for them, tell you they are not really John Tompkins but Johan de Tomb-cairns. Then, seeing no one was impressed, he went on, "All right, if you must hustle I'll miss the past and come to the present. As I said when I applauded your advice, fingers are the thing and I think we Lemurs have done well with ours and I must add in biological honesty that I have done far the best of all."

And with that the creature put out its hand. The group drew back. For the hand that was put out was like that of a living skeleton or worse. It was skinny as a dried up corpse and all the fingers had long unpleasant claws. But one finger was unbelievably grotesque. It had grown so long and thin that you might have thought it was nothing but a jointed skewer—and indeed, that was what it was, with a narrow, dirty, but needle-sharp claw at the end of it.

"Aye, aye," said the little monster, for that was his favorite remark, "I listened to your advice, Big Wings—I gave all my attention to the fingering as you said. And look—" The branch he was on was almost as shabby as himself, the bark had flaked and boring insects had riddled the wood. With speed and precision, as fast as a seamstress with a needle the Aye-Aye—for he has been called by the name he gave himself—darted in his lean living bodkin of a finger and brought out, impaled on the end of his nib-like claw a fat grub, popped the grub in its mouth and darted its claw into another hole. "Aye, aye," it called again, "you see I've learned my lesson Gabe. The finger is what we should grow. I've solved the problem. I drink fruit juice by sucking sugar cane. And what do I eat? These trees are nothing but larders of luscious food and all reserved for me, for no one else has had the sense to forge himself this neat key." And off it hopped, darting its finger into a hole and into its mouth as quickly as a really expert darner.[1]

"Pretty neat invention?" questioned someone, looking up at Gabriel.

"You think so?" he asked in reply. "I should have thought that it shows rather that it's never too late to go wrong. You see he had as good a hand as yours and he kept his attention on it. Right and good—it didn't turn into a hoof or claw. And then when he

had the secret, as you might say, in the palm of his hand, almost at his fingertips, he went wrong. That hand of his is done—he's sold out when he had all but got through. He and his whole family are going back."

"But why? They're not fierce blood-suckers nor just greedy guzzlers?"

"Well, I guess it's just because they wouldn't go on. It looks as though none of you is going to be let stay still anywhere, anyhow. The price of being noncommitted and unspecialized is that you have to keep on being more and more so."

At such a piece of angelic wise-cracking most of the group began to break away. Only Scratch-Scalp and a couple of his cronies hung on for centuries.

Gabriel went on, "Many of those Lemurs have as handy hands as yours. But somehow they're failing to handle them. Some can pick up things as neatly as you can. But, would you believe it, they're just too stupid to be able to pass what one hand has gotten hold of onto the other! They have to put down the tidbit and then, with their other paw, pick it up again. Which means, of course, that the tidbit may be snatched by someone else, or, if the dainty morsel is a succulent insect, then it will probably have hopped off on its own. While as to that absurd third finger of our self-distinguished friend, Aye-Aye, I wonder what bit of unbalanced

wish-power made that digit (which rightly should take third place in any whole hand's play) suddenly decide it would be the pointer? You point and poke naturally with your index finger and the other

fingers back it up. Do you think the Aye-Aye's third finger got sore at always having to play third fiddle and so decided it must be the big investigator all on its own—and just throw out the rest?"

"It is," said Scratch-Scalp, "a bit like the teeth that tusked on their own."

"Well, anyhow, it's plain, isn't it," went on Gabriel, "that the poor little fellow's spiked his gun with that silly finger-spike. He's crippled his hand (or let his finger cripple it) almost as much as though he'd turned it into a hoof. He's so certain that he must have his finger deeper in the pie than anyone else ever had, that really he's caught and trapped. So remember, even when you've grown past the risks and dangers of your budding points turning crabbed and cruel, you're not yet safe. Even when your hand hasn't turned into some clumsy hammer or silly weapon, you may yet be damned by a digit! Keep them all in play."

In the distance, monotonously, senselessly, the Aye-Aye echoed, "Aye, aye." Our group's assent to the Archangel's lecture was almost as automatic and unattending.

Even before he swept himself up into the sky with rainbow wheeling of wings and sun-flashing halos they had tucked their hands round their noses and gone to sleep. Their snores blended with the Aye-Aye's night-prowling wail.

The So-Heavy-Weight That He Gave
Up Standing

Nevertheless, when they woke again the group had apparently not lost the real gist of the lesson. It was still clear to them—at least at that level where you decide really what you'll be—that whoever was to win in the Life Race, had to avoid two things and learn two things. He mustn't be held up by trailing a tail—like people who now can't live in the present because they are always wanting to spin tales about their past. And, at the other end, he must avoid just as carefully the risk of being held up by pushing out monster teeth.[1] With these two tripping-up things out of the way, the next two things he had to learn were also at the two extremes of his person.

The first lesson had been pointed home to the group by the Aye-Aye. You must keep your hand whole and all your five fingers in full play, for the hand is a team and in a team each member plays for the rest. But the team play extends beyond the hand, indeed, all over the entire body; in fact, right to the furthest other end. So the second thing to be learned by our group at this point was to learn to walk properly, uprightly. For that's really the other end of the same proposition—its complement, as we say. Indeed, you never could be handy at your free end unless you were featly at your firm end. For to stand firm, right up on your feet, is a real feat—and no other animal has succeeded in doing it. Your foot is a wonderful holder that fits itself firmly on the earth so as to raise you and leave you free to reach up into the air and study the sky.

The notice in the front car of the Life Express now ran, "STAND-ING ROOM ONLY." If you wouldn't stand up you must get out and go down. Sooner or later you would be dropped for good. Certainly the lot that Gabriel was backing did manage to get that first point —not merely into their heads but right down to the bottom of their spines. For they did become, if not close cousins of the great Apes, something very like a limber form of that sort of person. That is to say, they drew in their tails and finally tucked them neatly in right under their skins. Where, of course, you still have one but would never so suspect, unless you fall on it, when it can hurt till you have no doubts about it being there. And with the temptation to hook up and anchor the-wrong-way-round, finally and for good out of the way, these people began to walk, stiffly and shamblingly, probably both, but walk they did. They were standing up for Life.

And as their legs straightened, at the end of them, instead of a kind of paw, there developed a real foot. Yes, it was that which let them grow a real hand with that wonderful super-swivel-finger, the thumb. The hand has had so much praise that it's really not fair to pass over the foot. For, but for the foot's very gallant and self-sacrificing subordination of itself, we'd never have had a hand to be so proud of. For the foot had to do something quite as won-derful, if not so spectacular, as the hand. The hand has undoubt-edly let us take hold of the world—and turn quite big pieces of its nice surface upside down. The foot has done as wonderfully by raising us so high that we can take a real outlook on the scene.

frightened than the others and when they were frightened they remembered it longer.

When the mammals rose above the reptiles they were given the queerly dubious gift of not being able to become unconscious directly it got cold. And anyone who has (and who hasn't) lain in bed wanting nothing so much but to go to sleep but is too cold to do so, can answer the question whether warm blood just in itself is an unmixed blessing. And now these big stiffly-walking, puzzledly-thinking half-men had found there's another chill even worse than the cold which comes because one has warm blood, and that is the cold of fear which comes because one has a big brain. And as little as warm blood in itself will keep you warm when it's cold, so little will a big brain keep you courageous when fear is lying all about like a subzero frost.

So when Gabriel spoke to their hearts—for, as the word shows, that's where courage is generated—and told them to stick it out— he didn't always get a cheer in reply.

"But to what end?" cried the deep life, far behind their eyes, the deep racial soul that could speak to him and he to it. "Are we never to have any real rest? Haven't we gone far enough, haven't we risked enough? Here, after fifty million years or so, here we are as defenseless really as babies. Here we are, literally up a tree! And still, as at the very beginning, we have to watch, half in puzzlement half in fear, all the great lords of the forest and the sward, of the river and the sea go past—and with that goddam Harpie Eagle, the lords of the air too—and we're still right out on the sidelines and hanging, as you might say, by a hair."

And Gabriel would answer, "Hang on, hang on! Believe me, you are really still on the main line and they are all off the tracks."

And they'd answer back, "But tell us then where we're going and what the end is to be. What are we to become?"

His great light would become flushed like a sunset topaz with

his deep concern for them, "Please, please don't ask that. Only
go on believing, go on trusting, go on being open, sensitive, kind,
wondering. Believe me, the end will be far more wonderful than
you could ever guess."

"But it hurts," they said, "hurts like hell. We just can't go on
unless you'll tell us why we should—always just going on, hanging
on, plodding on, on, on like this!"

And he would call back, "Please trust me. Don't you see you
have lasted longer than all the others even though you are so
weak—just *because* you are weak! Don't you see that you *have* been
looked after or by now you'd all be gone. Look, ever so many of
the others who seemed so strong—you remember that beast who
used to send you into a fit—the Sabre-toothed Tiger and ever so
many others—they're all gone."

But some muttered, "It's all luck really, just luck and our power
to creep away and not be noticed, but we're kept out in the shade
and shadow, crouching in the curtains round the feasting room
while the others have the time of their lives—really live."

"Heavens! I'd rather live well and then die," said one making
off, "and be strong just for once, than go on, aeon by aeon, in
this sort of fossil-rat condition—a creature that can neither live
nor die." And he loped off.

Those who remained could hardly stand it. "Gabriel," they called
shrilly.

And he glimmered like a faint rainbow over a distant mountain.
"Yes?" They ran toward him only to find that you never came up
with him—and then they stopped and whined. "If only you will
tell us frankly—do you know where we are going, do you know
what we are to become?"

And the rainbow became so faint that you didn't know its green
wasn't just the green of the grass, its blue that of some distant
water and its warm crimson only some dead leaves, while a voice

so faint you couldn't be sure it wasn't a falling breeze, replied, "No, I cannot tell you. No, I don't know. But . . ." and it rose to a gentle cool draft coming from some very high place—perhaps off keen snows. "He whom you must trust, He knows. I know this, He is never wrong. More, I know it is always a sign that He is going to prove unbelievably right when everything seems getting nowhere, getting impossibly hard and going irreparably wrong. And in yourselves you know—if you have the courage that reacts to the chill with a glow of faith—you know that it's going to be worth every doubt and shudder, though you may never explain how to your greedy blind selves."

The ice-cold air grew icier. It made several more shudder and shamble off to get out of it. A few, however, stuck and breathed it in deeply. They trembled but felt the stronger for their trembling.

But the ones who had winced at the cold and the uncertainty, and the challenge this inner and outer chill dealt their hearts, they went off south, always clinging to the shrinking jungle.

"Look," said Gabriel as he suddenly stood before those who were still holding their ground. The path that led south narrowed at that point between a frozen pool and a snow-sheathed cliff. Against the dazzling white background of the cliff-wall the Archangel stood like a giant prism of ice, flashing unbearably bright in the level sun yet tentative and shimmering as dew. Those who had shambled off south had actually brushed the hoar frost fringe of his robe, as they pushed blindly on and never suspected that he was touching them.

But now as the remainder looked and still didn't move, still hesitated against the wish to give up and follow the others, Gabriel suddenly clearly shone out at them. He was no flashing challenger to bar their way, to drive them back or to drive them on. He stood there, as once before, a great curve of question, asking them to ask themselves what it was that they really wanted, asking them to see whether the answer that the deserters were making really closed the question and proved there was no other way out? And as he bent, the great arc of his pure light became a lens.

"Look," he said, lending them his angelic lucidity, and their vision leaped up and they saw through his eyes. Far, far away now they picked out the straggle of the deserters. They had indeed retreated. They had now at last found a piece of stagnant forest-belt—just the sort of terrain the about-to-be men had feared for uncounted generations. Indeed, it was a place of swamped tangle-wood, steam and slush, very much like the not unnoisesome spot where, at the mammals' start, Gabriel had found huddled together the first of us . . . and called on us to run the long race we've been following in these stories—a four-score-million-year, long-distance, cross-country race.

The forest jungle was a dark, deadly place of Leeches and sting-ing Insects and tree-climbing Snakes and Leopards. The deserters' minds were full of fear and they hung always up in the branches, while underneath was the dark place out of which rose like a mist incessant terror, and into which if you fell you seldom if ever came back. So their arms became more and more like hooks—tending to grow as the Sloths had grown. They put their muzzles more and more right down on things and let their hands go hang. Their great lanky ropelike arms now hung down so far that finally these appendages had to be hoisted up and carried dangling when-ever their owners, and now almost embarrassed growers, ventured on the ground. That lot became the Gibbons. The others, with their snouty faces which wouldn't grow proper chins, creatures who could not pull their heads straight back and up onto the top of their spines, because they still liked to nuzzle at things and couldn't trust their spoiled hands, they became the Orangs and the Chimps. These, then, made for themselves a precarious tree-top refuge. They were literally driven out to the end of the branch; they were "out on a limb" of the Life Tree.

But there was one more deserter whose mistake was so big that he couldn't do even that—he couldn't even tree himself. He was that one who had gone off growling that all this sissy softness was no damn use. Here they had been kept waiting about with nothing but lots of vague talk (all right for someone who lived with his feet well off the ground), while all the time all the rest had been taking all the good places and by push and thews and toughness had gotten on and made him, and his sucker fellow-souls, just clear out. They could hear him still swearing to himself: he wasn't going to wait any longer—by hell and high water, he'd show them what was in him. He'd make a comeback that would leave not only all his sissy lot gasping—it would make all the others who thought they'd been so sharp and got the spring on you, give him a proper place and keep out of his way.

"So you see," it was Gabriel's voice as fine as the sound wind makes as it sifts the snow, "he's started off to remedy the blunder of waiting too long and keeping soft and supple. That's now his one big obsessional desire. And, of course, as long as he thinks in that sort of way, with that kind of brooding drive, with that sense that he's been wronged and this is the one way of getting his own back—why, of course, it works. It has always worked and always will. You've seen how many of them already have had the most unbelievable wishes. And done things with themselves which outwardly you would never have thought they could. And you'd have been ten times as sure they couldn't, if you could have seen, as I've been able to, what they had to do with their insides to make them back up their fancy outside notions. And this type is particularly interesting—do watch him well—for he's so like you, he kept on the main line so long. That is to say, he's getting his wish with all the pent-up self control and waiting-power, all the compound interest of waiting, piled up behind it. Do believe me, *just because you have waited* you are all much stronger really than the Whale, the Tiger or the Buffalo, the Rhino or the Elephant. And it's just that energy which now is going to blow up inside our friend and make a fairly neat and shapely person, able to turn his hands to most things and his interest on even more, into a brooding ogre. Look!" Gabriel suddenly called, for again he felt he'd talked a little too much without showing them a picture—a natural fault in one whose profession is that of an announcer. The magnification suddenly increased a thousandfold.

They saw a vast close-up. On the concave wall of the white cliff there loomed out at them the Gorilla's face. It was now black and ridged with great weals of muscle that made it into a sort of fixed and really rather pathetic grimace. Its huge mouth was thrust out infested with teeth so overgrown that they were practically no

use for eating but only for biting right through the body of any hapless enemy. And, it was clear that to work this giant jaw there had to be great straps of muscle that ran up to his eyebrows to get purchase and root on the big beetling edge there. So his poor little eyes were shut into a kind of cave. But even that wasn't enough. For in answer to the panic call for more violent defenses, a keel had grown along the top of his head—just like an overturned boat—so the jaw muscles, running right up there, might find still more purchase and root for themselves. But this heavy thatch of thews imprisoned the poor little brain underneath it so it could no longer think things out. It could only go on growling and feeling that something was wrong. You see, it was the silly teeth business again.

Just when the goal was in sight, when the little clambering Tree-Mouse[3] had grown into the promise of becoming a man, had already become a person who was walking freely everywhere, turning over things with his hands and judging them with his eyes and beginning to think . . . here then the poor Gorilla made the same mistake—or almost—as that made by that insane fighter, the Sabre-toothed Tiger.[4] You'll remember, his mistake was made long before by a still earlier savage-toothed swaggerer. In every case the teeth ended by attacking the very thing that grew them and evidently thought them up, the central nervous system, the brain. There was first that group of animals which carried their young in a pouch—one of them became a marsupial Tiger and ran his tiger-teeth right across the top of his skull in order that they might have hilts that would allow the longest possible blades. Then there was the Tiger that sprung from our lot, the mammals, and he, when he determined to be sabred, ran his tooth-roots right up his cheekbones. And now here's the Gorilla, someone nearly a man, and he's growing teeth that are quite tiger-looking and to hold the jaw that holds them he has to have straps of muscle right across the top of his head.

Gabriel brought the two other cases into his audience's mind as he showed them a magnified picture of the Gorilla's head. Then he turned to them and asked, "It's gloomy, I know, but do you see a gleam of hope? I do." But they couldn't, yet. Do you? Of course archangels see over such wide sweeps of time that they tend to catch sight of hope long before we who have to hop along on the ground have a notion that it's anywhere about. But if you ever want to have the fun they have, you'll find that it's found by finding grounds for hope.

The picture of the Gorilla's head was, of course, a talkie too, so they could hear him grumbling to himself, "I'm still terribly weak, I'm not nearly safe enough. I must be bigger. I must be stronger. Just look at the elephants, just think of the lions."

So he succeeded in shutting up his head just as the lion had succeeded in manacling its paw which might have been a true hand. Then the picture grew larger still and the group found itself looking into that cavern under the beetling brow-ridges, past the scowling mask and above those terrible jaws. And they saw, looking out at them, two eyes, so sad, so miserable, so skulking, that all the parent heart of them suddenly felt—as sharp as stepping on a thorn—a stab of pity. They saw at once that was the way one of the babies looked if it got lost for a moment in the dark. To get it out of its panic, they knew you had to hold it fast to yourself to melt the sharp icicle of fear that had formed in its heart. There was no other way, they knew that without a doubt.

And to their inner thought they heard the voice of the Archangel in antiphon chanting, "There is no other way. But that way goes through all the shut gates."

But the gorilla did not hear—he did not wish to for some reason best known to himself. And they could not get to him, for when

they stood back and studied him, he looked so forbidding, so terribly strong—they were frightened of their own puniness. You see, they, too, were allowing, in a way, that he was right; he was strong and they were weak. But the other way round was the real truth. They did try to see the little needy child in him again. It was lost, buried under that black avalanche of muscle and sullen determination not to trust to any kind of sloppy softness any more. And under the weight of his stupid resolution, which was like a millstone round his neck, he went down and down . . . down to the ever more enervating south . . . sinking plummetlike, ever deeper, past the Gibbons and the Chimps and the Orangs even. He was so blindly heavy, he had such a dead weight of defeat in his soul that it sunk him right down and out from even the arrested protection of the trees.

"Look," Gabriel was speaking again and the magnification now showed the Gorilla's figure full scale, "look," said the snow-calm voice, "he's possessed by such an insane passion for strength, he's so frightened of being thought weak and timid, that he simply can't stay in the branches that would have given him some refuge. Remember, that's the way the wish-power has to work. He who wills the end wills the means. You've seen again and again, haven't you, that all the others who have gotten their wishes asked for things that you, and indeed, I, would have thought really impossible. And they would have been, had not the wish-power in you been real creative power. It has been able to make the most unbelievable inventions—and had to—to meet the insane silliness of the desires of the fools who wouldn't wait to see what would really make them happy, who wouldn't ask whether there might be a big all-over will in which they could all find fulfillment. You remember the Whale and how he got over the bends? And so it goes on, and so it must go on until someone asks to know the right way rather than to get his own way. That's why the Gorilla has had to become too strong, too heavy. Even the patient trees can't bear his weight now, the branches can no longer break his fall, they have to let him down. But the ground can't be a haven for him. For all of you know the ground isn't any longer a rest place or a roost—it's a runway. Those of you who have come down to it must be ready to run the race and be in constant training to run it. You've got two devils to act as whippers-in. Back of you now are all the deserters who made up their minds that to prey on you with their mis-wish-grown weapons was better than going ahead. And inside yourself is the same devil—always telling you that you've been a fool and that you too could grow weapons (as indeed at any time you can)—and then you could teach them all a lesson (which of course you would)—though those are the lessons no one ever seems to learn from, least of all those who inflict them! Oh yes, indeed, your cousin, the Gorilla, has made a comeback—though I'd call it a go-back. He's ready now to take on the Leopard and the Lion on their own ground and he has the fine feeling of seeing them decline battle. But you see his victory hasn't made him happy, has it?"

They looked at the gloomy, suspicious, frightened face.

"Surely you can't say he's any more light and gay in his figure than in his frame of mind?"

They looked at the heap of muscle that was squatting on the ground. It went from the pineapple top of the little wizened brain, spreading like a melting ice cream to the spread-out eyebrows, spreading again to the still wider jaws and then on downward—there was no sign of a neck—to vast shoulders and vaster chest with great roots of arms coiling out—and then there was nothing more. That monstrous weight had buckled the poor little legs.

"Dear me," said one of the onlookers, "he's dumped himself on the ground by his weight, just as the tuskers pushed themselves out of touch with the tusks they thought were going to push everything about as they liked!"

"Yes," answered Gabriel, "you see, if you weigh as much as that, well, you can't carry all that on just two legs with two small sticks of lime inside them. Either you have to go down on all fours for good or-you have to squat like a cripple. That's the way he's driven himself into a self-made corner."

And while the Archangel of the Annunciation and the Final Record told the story, beside his crystal clear figure appeared another, a kind of identical twin or complement. For Gabriel was all gold and green and this other figure was entirely sapphire blue and ruby. In his hand was a vast instrument sometimes mistaken for a spear, sometimes for a sword. In real fact, when you look close at it, it's a great Balance. For Michael, the Archangel who calls out the rating and finds the weight and drive of every soul after his brother Gabriel has told its story, Michael being a son of the All Father, does not fight enemies or execute criminals.[5] He weighs . . . and the soul of its own gravity of desire then slides off the great slope of that beam of justice. No one gives it even a push or jog. Under nothing but its own impetus it goes with gathering momentum along the line and on the grade that it itself has chosen.

As our lot watched, on that great swaying runway, they saw the Gorilla crouch down and swell till, true enough, his poor little legs actually gave way under the weight and he slid helplessly further down to the lower end of the beam that dipped into darkness. He weighed in so heavily to counterattack the fanged and clawed animals, that the onlookers saw him roll along until he was lost among the fighting beasts, until he had become a man-parody of a Tiger. And yet all the while, as he sank into the shadow, out of his fierce face they saw the two small frightened eyes of the terror-struck child, looking for someone to save it, reassure it, love it. For deep down in his actual nature he was not yet lost. He was imprisoned, and in the dark of a clouded mind still wishing to escape. His hand did not become taloned. He did not want to destroy others, only to defend himself against the destroyers. He did not want their blood but only to repel the attack he feared. And he knew no other way but that of counter-violence. He did not want their flesh—he shrank from such a thing as from poison.

All he wanted was to live where he could live unmolested, absolutely safe, finally completely secure.

Gabriel pointed out to the group this poor squat crouching figure creeping along Michael's great earth-spanning beam and finding at last high mountain plateaus where the wild celery grows in thick meadows of lush stalks. There the poor fugitive looked about him. The climate was cold and damp on these cloud-wrapped heights. But, after all, that was safer. He would browse all day—for, as the AA explained, you have to take in celery by the cartload if you are to keep six or seven hundred pounds of bone and muscle in fighting trim. And you have to become willing to have whole reservoirs of rain poured on you. Since you are too stupid to cultivate such vegetable gardens yourself, they must be superirrigated if you are not to eat them down to the bare earth.

As night fell . . . they watched through the telescopic lens of Iris and saw the great shambling monster come in with the gathering dusk. As he waddled through the celery beds the group could hear, through the swish of the rain, his feet and hands squelching in the mud. For his weight was so heavy that he was practically going on all fours. Finally, at the foot of a tree he sat down and roared for his family to join him and tried to rid his front paws of the clay. They saw his knuckles had callouses on them, great pads of leather-hard skin, just like you see on the feet of men who walk shoeless all their lives on rough ground. The family began to gather. The mothers and the young swarmed up the tree and arranged some kind of bough-and-twig hammock. But father had to stay below. No branch would bear him and he well knew that if he fell he would need no other blow to break his bones. Mother Earth would have given such a buffet to her errant child that he would have had to lie still for good on her unfeeling breast. The dark came down; the torrential rain poured. The poor huge beast gathered fronds, large leaves and sprays of branches and tried to

make itself a rude nest. There, he snored uneasily through his great flattened nostrils, while every now and then some smell would shake him into conscious fear. Then he would beat on his breast and bellow, to warn whoever was within smell-shot that dinner would be bought too dearly here.

The vast balancing beam held by Michael,[6] the scale that spans all time and along which we are all trekking one way or the other, along which the little group had watched the Gorilla's retreat, began to fade. The azure and ruby figure who sustained the balance, vanished. Only Gabriel was left with them and he was more golden than green for now the winter sun was very low and the snow very cold.

However . . . just before they made off for their tree, one of the group turned back. It was slow, hesitant Scratch-Scalp again. "Gabriel," he called to the figure that was nearly transparent.

"Yes, friend? What, partner?"

"Well, I know I've asked it before. But still, can't anything be done for him? You see, he was so lately one of us. And you know, it would be so easy for any of us to have gone that way—just let a thought brood in one's mind and then it goes on almost of itself, boring deeper till it's lost to sight. It settles in as a tick does if you don't groom yourself over when you come in from the bushes. One's just aware of it as a grievance, a notion that it's about time one did get one's way for once in a lifetime, one ought to get a little of what is due to one . . ." The slow chap was really talking to himself.

But he was roused by Gabriel remarking, "Oh, you've discovered that?"

And in a flash he knew that he'd known it always in a way, deep down. "But can't anything be done?"

Gabriel waited, as though the question wasn't finished.

And the other felt the waiting, the gentle tension of the unspoken counter-question, the delicate pull as when a spinner draws out a thread. So, in a moment the end of the question came up, as a fish does on the end of a line, into the clear-lit part of his mind, and he said quite quietly in spite of the sounding absurdity of it, "Can't I, couldn't I do anything, do something for him?"

Gabriel didn't laugh, he didn't leave. He gathered round him in a moment something of that tremendous silence that is more full of power, more full of information, more full of solutions than all the committees reading out aloud all the text books in all the world. It is called "The Awful silence that is before the Throne," the hub and pivot of the whole creation.

When you look at a great dynamo, spinning so fast and yet so smoothly you can hardly be sure it's not still, spinning as effortlessly as a sleeping top, and all the while pouring out a torrent of invisible energy, swifter, stronger, more penetratingly irresistible than the fullest of tides—then you have a faint, very very faint, the very faintest weakest notion or shadow of that centralest Centrifuge, that uttermost Dynamo, the sparks of which are all the outrushing nebulae and island universes as they whirl out and away to the final limit of Space-Time. For there, at that perfectly powerful Center, there is no friction, no cross-questioning, no debating, disputing, contriving. There is complete and ultimate presence of mind, of heart, of will. Someone said that he heard it last for half an hour. But it seems that all he meant was that he was able to stand it for some thirty minutes—after which, as a kind of protection against that intensity of completion, that perfection of meaning, he himself had to start arguing and illustrating and reasoning. For none of us could endure it as we are, and that is the reason why we are what we are, always in some sort of hurry to get out of some sort of tangle, always wanting to get something done or undo something we think has been done wrong. If we could stand it for more than thirty minutes perhaps we'd never come back to tell people anything about it; perhaps we, too, would become so completely, perfectly present that no one would ever again notice

that we were about.[7] For that is what is called contemplation and that is why it is said, by those who know, to be so much more powerful than any action.

When Gabriel saw that the hesitant one had had all he could stand, the Archangel Friend didn't break that silence, for that silence can't be broken. With the immense strength of his almost unsurpassed power he raised again the corner of its pressure which he had let glide out into that small mind.

The little creature breathed again. He was out once more on that little teeter-totter of lung and heart which keeps us rocking to and fro, seeing and reflecting. *A swinging wicket set between the seen and the unseen.*

The Archangel, brighter than the last splendor of the sunset, stood between his small partner and the Eternal Imageless Splendor, and, without knowing that he was being shielded, the animal found it could think again and could gaze on the archangelic brightness with the quiet reflective relief with which we gaze at a calm candle flame. "Scratch-Scalp," said Gabriel, speaking, of course, so closely, intimately, right inside the slow one's mind that the Silence remained as clear as ever, "Scratch-Scalp," the voice was no more really than the Silence changing key from content to interest, "do you notice any difference between the tuskers and this latest tough that has weighed in?"

"Why this one is still one of us," Scratch-Scalp answered the Archangel in the same silent speech. "He has become a bit of a monster. He's just too big, true enough, too big for his poor feet. But he hasn't magicked himself into a complete mess so far—he's only playing a joke of a sort."

"You mean that he's still obviously your kind, your kin, and so you feel kind to him?"

"Well, he's still got hands—not hoofs—and teeth—not tusks. But—"

"But what?"

"Mustn't it depend on whether he wants to come back?"

"You mean that if he still feels strong and you look weak, why should he want you to be kind to him or to give him anything?"

"Yes, he certainly can take anything he wants."

"Anything, everything but what he really needs."

"What's that?"

"The need to be ready to take from others."

"Then do you mean we should start—I could only start by giving my wish-power to something that was willing to ask me?"

"It would take quite a lot of trust on both sides, wouldn't it?"

"It would have to start with my being—" Scratch-Scalp's voice went slower and slower till, like a running-down clockwork it stopped on two words, "touched . . . moved."

"Yes," said the Archangel, "yes, I think you know the answer now. Though I realize you couldn't tell even me—so I can't be really sure you really know. It will depend, won't it?" he said in the tone that two pioneers might talk to each other of a trip they were planning through unknown country but with a pretty good horse sense of the lie of the land that would confront them. "It all depends."

And the still rather monkeylike person said as quietly as though he were talking to an equal, "Yes, I guess it will. I guess it turns on whether I can hold out for the last lap—and then wish—"

"What?" asked the Archangel with real curiosity in his voice, "What?"

"Wish," said the other very slowly as though he were counting the cost, even wondering whether he could pay it, but seeing that you couldn't get there for less, "wish nothing for myself."

"Done," said the Archangel in the same voice he had used to end the proto-mammals' captivity under the Dinosaurs at the very start and so had started the great mammal age, "done," and he shot like a meteor right back into the sky which was already shivering with frosty stars.

"Come along," shouted the group who already had arrived at the tree and were getting into their nests and roosts, "come along, old lag-behind, always talking to yourself—and besides, didn't you hear that roll of thunder? Odd on a winter night, but looks as though we'd have a storm."

But there wasn't a storm. Instead there were such wonderful northern lights that while the others snoozed, Lag-Behind got up and watched them, shivering a little out on the end of a branch till finally a huge star came close to the earth and went in behind a hill. Lag-Behind thought it must be a messenger of some sort— and when he was back in his own hole in the huge trunk, he dreamed he saw himself with a couple of friends trekking out quickly over the snow to where the star was shining behind the hill—and somehow when they got there ever so many of the beasts he'd feared were there. But he didn't fear them any longer and they were friendly too and led him on to where they were all gathered round looking at something. But the rest of the dream (when he woke in the clear frosty morning) he couldn't remember, though he was sure somehow that sometime he would. And just that feeling made him oddly glad.

Part III

STORIES OF THE PERSON WHO GAVE AWAY HIS WISH

The One Who Stood Up for Good

The weather remained bad. Indeed, it became quite outrageous. Even the bravest had to yield step by step. But they never let it become a rout. They disputed every retreat. All the northern trees they had clung to died in their tracks. But some of the southern trees were as stubborn die-hards as the best of the beasts. There came a time when the foul weather stopped becoming fouler. Some trees had adapted. They learned actually how to like the cold, how to store energy and get rid of insect pests during the hardest months and then break into fresh leaf, flower and fruit in the heavy spring rains and the short, hot summers.

And the beast who stuck it out best clung near to these fruit trees.[1] He was still very like a rather limber-limbed ape and his thoughts were still nearly all hunches or happy accidents. But it was clear that something in him was winning. True enough, he was still generalized, he was still without tusks or talons, fangs, spurs, spines or stings. But he hadn't stood still, or rather he wasn't crouching still. He had advanced. He was steadily learning to stand up straighter and straighter.

The group looked at one another . . . and as they looked, more and more often that chuckle came in their throats when something odd happened, something they couldn't understand and could have been frightened by. Haven't you ever suddenly, for no apparent reason, found yourself laughing? Or when you looked at something you knew ever so well, haven't you suddenly seen it newly as though for the first time? It was that way with them. Suddenly you saw the tree . . . and new leaves breaking out all over it . . . very pale, delicate, shimmering in the level dawn light and you found yourself almost sheepishly smiling. It was the the same sort of feeling when you came across the baby playing with its toes or just met another person coming back to the tree. Later again when the last fruit was gathered and the autumn sun set with dark storm clouds taking it and a bitter sighing wind coming up from the night, you sighed too. And perhaps then someone would begin a moaning cry that grew to a lament and you felt you must die. But your eyes at that moment filled. You held onto each other, you rocked and sobbed and finding relief and answer, you slept. Laughter and tears had come to bestow on man two strange gifts which always seem silly to the tough. Yet they are essential elements of that resilient "temper" which, like the temper of steel, has given to man out of all the creatures, his incomparable power of suppleness and recovery.

The weather called for cloaks. Gradually you added a bit of an old skin to some roughly twisted tough grasses. The long straws of the grain which you ate, you played with, making frills, aprons, stiff shoulder shawls, hats even when it was hot and wider ones when the rain pelted down. You hunted over the tree to find insects and those trees you groomed most, bore fruit best. So you clung to them persistently. You trimmed off the lower shoots to eat the small succulent leaf and the removal of these suckers and lower twigs and sprays helped the tree too, by this happy-go-lucky pruning.

But, however distracted the group might be in detail, however confused, inept, unintentional in any one activity, always some kind of drive or draw kept on shepherding them. Their steady growth in upstandingness was one of these main central drives. They would keep on looking up, stretching up. And once again, if only an onlooker could have looked long enough he would have detected an archangel figure leaning down and over. But to see that aeonic figure, that superbeing who could see the spirit of each animal species and speak with it and draw it out, one would have to live on his vast time span and be as patient as he who is nearly as patient as God Himself. One would have to become as tirelessly observant as those night-long patient photographic plates in observatories that gaze all through the dark at just one black spot in the star sky and there, when they are developed, there this sensitive stuff has gathered on its surface enough photons of light to build up a picture of a star that is really out there but no one can ever see it. For no human eye could bear to be so patient in watching. Our flickering, blinking eyes would break down into blindness even attempting such gleaning of the last grains of ultra light.

So, too, our little feverish flick of interest cannot watch even one hour of a species' life. But if we could—well, at this point we should have seen the great figure enticing these fellows of the fruit trees ever to stretch and span more. And yet it must be a reach which never grew unbalanced, like the all-too-arm-spanned apes with their poor little legs and equally poor grasp of hand. So Gabriel bent again over his increasingly loved model. For the fewer that endured, the more he loved those who hung on. He touched the back, still wavering from neck to loin, as once he had stroked the little trial mammal's scales and left him with a fur coat. He rippled his golden finger, full of divine vitality, down the groove of the spine, down that wonderful chain of dice bones that can set and stand like an oaken post or curl like a ship's cable. Then he paused a moment. Just below the very middle of the back. Sure enough, under that touch the back dimpled, curved in as a cat curves its back in with pleasure as you stroke it. But because the touch was an Archangel's the effect lasted. There was a new strength and resilience in the spine. And through that new balance the body was able to rear and poise itself on a new straightness, a new uprightness.

"Oh, that's graceful," cried several standing round.

"Well, wish it," called their shining friend.

They looked about shyly, then wished and sure enough felt their spines gather under them like powerful springs.

"It'll be awfully tiring on the feet," criticized a cautious hesitant.

Gabriel touched the instep of his model's foot with the tip of one of his flame-feather pinions. And once again, exactly as a cat will arch up its back with pleasure to get nearer your stroking finger, the foot arched and once more and again, when the glowing touch had passed, the spring remained. The flame-feather swept right up and flipped playfully the person standing at attention, right on the tip of his nose. He started back as anyone does when delicious but really far too strong smelling salts suddenly prick our scent-buds. It's like a needle touching one's brain. And as the playfully assaulted model flicked back his head, in went his till-then-out-thrust chin, forward came his forehead. His face stood as finely upright as his body. His head balanced like a final fruit of knowledge on the delicate shaft of his neck. His eyes looked out steadily level across the world to the farthest horizon.

"Raise your hand," called the Archangel. He obeyed. "Now put your thumb right over on your palm." It was done. And again, but now quietly, gently, Gabriel said, "Done! There! That is all that is needed. That is the one movement that is required to conquer the world, to unlock all earth's treasures. With that He gives you the key—the master key all the other animals fumbled with, failed to understand. You see, they've all twisted its precious simplicity into cunningly fatal forms. They turned it into hoofs, paws, claws. From the false side-fins of the Whale to the grotesque third finger of the Aye-Aye they have all degraded the open hand with which they were to have greeted life into a mean tool for private selfish satisfaction. But for you, now, there's no end to the things that can be found and can be done with that exploring, trusting tentative hand. Now everything is possible to you. The Kingdom of Heaven upon earth now lies open to you, if you will enter with that key. But remember, this hand is the most magical thing upon earth, an instrument of unknown potential. No one (certainly not I) dare say what it may not do. For it is, indeed, a model, or shadow, of that Hand which shaped this world. See then, oh, see well, that it does only and always His will here on earth as it is done in Heaven."

Then, seeing that they didn't have much of an idea as to what he was driving at, and suspecting that he was sounding perhaps a little prematurely pompous, if not minatory, Gabriel called out,

"Now for some foot-work as pretty as the hand. Don't despise your feet—without their loyal support you'd be back at your original almost-all-fours."

He swooped out into the open, skimming the earth as a big Kestrel will sometimes parcel over a field looking for a field Mouse or two. And they ran out after him trying to catch the great lazy sweep of pinion. He made them race faster and faster, until they almost ran down a young small horse and Gabriel had to sweep his wing in between the hunters and hunted to let the panting four-footed quarry get away. Then back again they ran across the short grass, crisp with still-frozen dew—racing one another to the tree, tingling as though on fire with new life. And sitting down at the base of the great trunk—for it was a chestnut—they rooted out stores of the nuts they had hidden in clefts made by the great wreathed roots, and caches and pockets of corn, grain and small dried fruits and roots.

They chawed away, gabbling in their excess of enjoyment, as a merrily boiling pot bubbles over. One would leap up and hop over another, two would seize hold of each other's wrists and spin round. Every now and then an eddy of rhythm would catch up the entire group and make it circle, as a whole area of dried leaves will be taken with an invisible gust and go waltzing like a single figure down the glade. They did not see Gabriel—indeed, now they saw him less and less clearly. It was getting, you see, more and more like that moment when you discover that you really are in the rainbow though you can't see it, while others see you actually part of it, all lit and iridescent in its many colors. As it happens he was never nearer to them than then. He was actually in their weaving hands and in the bright iris of their eyes that shone with such friendliness, such fun, such wonder.

How Sticks Became Hands And Stones Teeth

When the group began to play with the sticks and stones on the ground, these dull little things themselves began to come alive, ceased to be merely rubbish. And as the group played and fiddled with increasing fun, they found first that their reach was growing. The stick in your hand became a wonderful long arm, and when you found one with a hook at the end of it, it became actually a hand. It explored up into the tree bringing down nuts you'd seen but never could get to. Then came the turn of the stones. They were smaller but so much harder. Hardest of all were sullen black ones. But if you gave them a sudden crack the right way they'd splinter. That left an edge so sharp you could cut things that otherwise you could never gnaw or tear apart. They found edges that cut, edges that sawed and points that pierced. And as they gazed at these things, which till then had been just so much in-the-way rubble, they heard Gabriel's voice right behind them as soft as the smallest breeze in the highest spray of a tree in springtime.

"Do you see? Now you have all that the poor deserters thought to get, but got caught by. You've got detachable claws and teeth and endlessly replaceable ones too, and you have them well out

in view of your eyes, so you can see what you're tackling, and nicely out of the way of your tongue so you don't bite it!"

And when they had climbed up into the tree for an afternoon siesta it was Gabriel that persuaded them to take quite a store of these promising playthings with them aloft.

"You've often had fun, you remember, dropping nuts on the backs of the stupid cattle and making them start and scamper? Now toss them out farther! Look, the stone is flying. Go on— give it a bigger start. Look, you made it travel. Now throw that stick. It's gone far farther. Try, all of you, if you can hit that log lying out there."

It was some distance out—most of them got nowhere near. But they were now a competing team. The stick-throwers were first the weaker side but soon they learned tricks to gain on the stone-throwers, till one found how to fling a stick by first putting it into another stick that you held in your hand and whirled. But that made the stone throwers inventive, too. They began to put their stones in long pouches of soft bark and so sent off their missiles with a whirl that took them right beyond the log. It was great fun, such fun that everyone began making collections of good sticks and suitable stones. And the best round smooth stones were good, too, for sharpening the stones that were found with natural blades.

The Finding Of The Friend In The Fire

You filed and tapped away till several times you heard Gabriel at the back of your mind saying, "Did you see that? There and there!" It was true something popped out for a minute like a very small piece of sunlight—it was a spark. But it had to hop and gleam and die hundreds and thousands of times before you tumbled to what it was—fire. For, of course, fire is the one thing that, as long as you are an animal, you must not even think about. You can go way back into the sea and become again a sort of monster fish—and climb up even onto the air with your hands and turn into a kind of tiny recollection of an extinct flying lizard— and you can become a four-footed mowing machine and a blood-sucking parasite and a kind of monster worm pursuing worms in underground tunnels. You can go on land almost as fast as the wind, and through the depths of the sea as though you hardly could drown. You can go up on the wind itself, up into the still evening air. You can push your way deep in the dense soil till you live in its dark damp pack, as though you were a root. Earth, sea and air, the three elements are yours. But the fourth, fire, you may not even touch. With terrible pain he punishes you if you go even near him and marks and mars you for your daring. If he catches you where you cannot escape him, then the cry of your agony is

never forgotten by those who got away—and of any other trace of
you there remains none.

Fire is annihilating agony, far worse than drowning or falling
smashed on the earth, far worse than starving, far worse than being
torn to pieces by one of your fellows who has turned into a blood-
lusting devil. So there is no beast but looks upon it as the mysterious enemy and when it is present even the fiercest becomes craven.

One day a section of the group was out rather too far afield.
It had been a lean season for everyone and it was necessary to
glean a wide stretch of country to get enough back into store. It
was late in the autumn but yet no rain had come to make anything
shoot even a little before the frosts. They trampled through the
dried-up bushes and never a nut or root could they see. But, round-
ing a big clump of bushes they caught a smell that stiffened them.
Gabriel had with a wave of his wing shifted a wandering breeze
so it blew toward them, not from them. They crept round on
hands and knees and sure enough, down a small glade they saw
a tigress with her cubs. She was lean with starvation and the cubs
tugged at dry teats. She was growling with desperation. Had they
been twice as numerous and really armed she would have attacked
and died rather than let them go. They swung round in their
tracks and began to lope along as silently as they might. If only
they could go like this for, say, several hundred heartbeats, down
this slope and over the other crest they would be safe. But once,
twice, three times their feet snapped dry branches. The sticks
cracked like betraying signals. And they heard the tiger's moan
turn into delighted rage. Another roar told them she was already
well on their tracks. They could move fast when in terror and they
had a start. If their breath didn't give out they might get away.
But they could hear their pursuer crashing through the break
behind them. Somehow they managed to breast the rise, almost
blind with the effort and the following death now not far from

springing distance. They threw themselves down the ridge's other side. It was almost clifflike. They rolled headlong crashing down through the bushes only to find themselves blinded and choking—the valley below was aflame.

How do forest fires start? Mostly by people lighting them, or by the sun shining through a piece of glass and making a burning focus-spot, or by lightning. But this was none of these. Could it have been Gabriel? Perhaps so. Archangels are, after all, made of fire and they teach us not merely by singing carols but by fireworks. The group wheeled round. Had they lived long enough to make gloomy proverbs—which providentially they hadn't—they would have remarked that they were between the devil and the deep—while in point of fact they were between fire and one of their erstwhile fellows who had turned cannibal. As they stalled, their enemy leaped down among them. They all drew up, the smoke choking them, the fire already in blasts singeing them. They howled with terror and so did their fellow beast. For the bluff they had thrown themselves over was too steep to climb up again, at least in that moment which was all the fire would yield them. Then once again the wind turned—and was on their side; it blew down the bluff strongly away from them. And the cruel fire, who cares for no fang or claw and makes the mightiest muscle writhe and shrivel like a withering leaf, the fire bowed before the invisible almost inaudible voice of the wind, or the Presence that was in the gentle cool wind, bowed and retired, as the brimming tide bows and draws off the wide beaches as the far small white moon tells it to come back into the deep.

They coughed and gasped and cried more than a little and then heard beside them another whimper, a fellow whimper. It was their once fellow creature, and though their fear had been great, hers was greater, so great that she could not move, could not scale the bluff. But they found the greater terror had burned

out the lesser and, even more, had made them all kin in front
of this raging, implacable blind death. She drew to them shuddering, for in front, though the flames came no nearer, the fire sent
out gusts of choking vapor. They saw she could not get back up
the slope and at any moment the command of the wind might
be withdrawn—again the death of utter agony would be upon
them all. They turned to climb the slope and found without
knowing it, that they were helping their exhausted fellow of the
four paws and the frightful teeth up the bluff. They pulled at
her coat as she panted and slipped and shuddered with palsying
terror. They got her to the top and she shambled off to her poor
cubs. They could not strike her, nor could she maul them. The
peace of the common peril was on them both. And as they
scuttled home and looked at the great column of angry smoke
that swayed in the uncertain air, they were not certain that out
of that pillar, half of flame, half smoke, there was not looking at
them an eye which they had thought they knew but now wondered
whether they had ever really understood. Yet when that memory
had lost part of its stunning power, so that in the mind the first
gleams of reflection could appear, they began to think back over
their adventure.

One day then, not long after the sparks appeared, as the black
glossy stones were struck to give them fresh edges, a new spark
of attention answered in the dark background of their minds.
They were interested, so they tried to catch the little glancing
thing. And one day someone did . . . The tiny star like a bright
insect hovered twisting on the piece of grass on which it had lit.
When it died and they had made many more, they learned how
to feed it from grass to grass, and so on to leaves and twigs. It
really was fun and it didn't try to bite you if you didn't touch it.
And if it became too big and willful, why then you could be the

wind yourself. You just gave a big puff and either it bent away, quite frightened, or you just killed it outright.

No one succeeded in catching it and making it perch with you up in the tree. It was always on the ground among the stones; there it hopped out and winked at you and you played with it. When you went up to roost, you put it to bed couched round with some stones.

If you were clever, there it was lurking, if a little faint, in the morning. But often it was gone and had hidden itself somewhere and you had as much difficulty in making it wake up as trying to rouse a winter tortoise. So gradually, in order to save the trouble of rousing the spark every morning, some of you stayed down in a low crotch near it and took turns to keep an eye on it and when it looked like dying, you dropped bits of peat near it so that it could doze away quietly like yourselves. That led to making a regular bed and seat for it where this your strangest of friends could sit safely, for him and for you. In turn that led you to making your seat and bed near his stone one. It was warmer there than up the tree. It became a regular duty for someone to sit, whether it was night or day, by the red-eyed friend and see that he was kept cheerful. You said people mustn't blow him out, they must feed him with the food he liked. And when he got low you found further that you could make him, like a sick one of yourselves, get back his strength if you fed him very gently and breathed encouraging words over him.

"You'd never have thought it possible, would you?" said the voice of Gabriel. Lifting up their eyes they could see his eyes looking down at them through the column of fire-tinted smoke that swept up from the fire-throne stones. Sure enough those were the eyes, though much smaller, that had looked out for the great column of the forest fire. "You'd never have thought, would you, that this person would have become your friend? Do you realize that he is keeping you gently warm during these cold nights?" and he ruffled his great plumes against the frosty sky. "Do you realize how much better the nuts taste when he has first had a nibble at them and do you see how you all gather round him as though he were the host of the party and how he is teaching you, more than earth, water or air could teach you? Now look over your shoulders."

Sure enough, away in the dark they could see green eyes watching them and big padding forms pacing to and fro. "None of them can come near you, provided the terror you have made your friend keeps quiet watch for you while you sleep safe through the night, safe and warm." They looked and sure enough it was true, though it had all grown on them as imperceptibly as a clear, very early summer dawn. "So," said Gabriel, "you see you have now crossed one of the biggest of frontiers, almost the last in your long trek— while the earth has spun some sixty million times round the sun. You have left the beasts behind forever. You have come into the light that now will go with you all round the dark night cycle. When I first came to you I came to give you the first gift of Him who never slumbers or sleeps but is always watching all His creation with a love that is as wise as it is powerful. For the

Lizards, you remember, had to lose consciousness directly the air got too chilly. You have stayed aware of the light as long as the sun was up, even though it mocked you from a wintry sky. But with night you slept, or if you had to be awake then you crept along by your ancient night sight. Now you will have light to go with you. You shall carry a little sun, part of the sun's stored energy with you, and you shall strike a light when you wish and you will see the world lit by it as the sun shows it, though more dimly. But you must lose in order to gain. Look round again at those flashing emerald eyes. Wherever you see that green light you will recognize a night-seer, a prowler and tracker. That light, that sinister glow is now gone from your eyes.[1] You are human, they are animal; you have crossed the stream that none has crossed save you. This is the river of fire. This is your baptism of flame and that is why you saw me in the terror of the forest fire. This, then, shall be your altar. At the hearth here you shall worship Him who is invisible fire. For as the fire will make your garbage clean, your food tasty, your bodies warm, your sleep safe, so it is your friend and symbol of His friendship to you, one more of His gifts which he sends me to announce to you. Now that He has granted this gift he denied all His other creatures, now that he has put creative destruction into your wonderful hand, take heart for the love of man," and the voice was loud like the roar of the forest fire, "and take care for the Love of Heaven. For remember," the voice became still more terrible, though more distant, as they looked up and saw the smoke rising into the height of the stars, "remember, though you know Him as your Friend, remember that you know Him not at all in Himself. Know that you may know him through His gifts, if you use them as He has used them to you, as gifts and loving-kindnesses to others. But remember," and once more the voice was a roll of thunder, "you know Him in no wise as He is and dare not face Him even as the angels alone

dare face Him, through the cloud of the Living Light. For when
that cloud lifts then even we must quail."

And the wild beasts bayed, seeking their meat and the fire beat
down on the little hearth-group singeing them and stifling them
with smoke, as they shuddered and huddled one to another.

The Wolf That Was Not Kept from the Door

The fire had settled down on the hearth. It had become the very center of the family life. The small ones loved to come so near it now that you had to teach them their manners toward it. To look into its clear waving colors you would have thought it had all the gentle freedom of the air, the flow and freshness of the water, and the friendliness of the sun combined with the warm sweet glow of your mother's cheek. But you had to learn to keep your distance. Up to a certain point it was everyone's friend, making a genial warmth through the whole house. Further, those who knew it well, like your mother—she could cook with it and it would make the food wonderful. Flour turned into bread coming out of the oven golden brown and so fragrant your mouth watered. Your father with his cunning tools, could play with it in even more ways. He would work with it, giving it that hardest thing, metal, and the fire would take it and make it soft for him till he could then turn it into all kinds of wonderful new tools. And the metal flushed like a flower in the flame and sounded and shaped like clay when it came out of that magic, till it went black and there once again you had metal ringing and cutting like nothing else on earth. And at the opposite end of things, you could use mud, muddy clay that would take your every touch, take any shape you wished, so you could make every sort of cup, pitcher, vase or bowl. Of course, though, they'd be soft and useless. But let them dry and then put them in the fire—out they came glowing red, hard as stone. If you didn't break them they'd last a lifetime, carry water from the well, hold the oil and the wick and so make the fire into little portable suns and stars you could carry with you at night, and store the grain in great jars with lids safe from the mice and rats.

But the wisest of all those round the hearth were your grandparents. They no longer worked with the flame but they sat by it and they told you to see in the depths of the glowing charcoal all kinds of lit-up wonder worlds. When you so gazed, right at the end of great glowing halls you saw then a wonder figure with great wings and they said, "Do you see," and when you whispered, "Yes," they whispered back, "Listen now, and he will speak."

And you heard when the house was very still through the quiet fluttering of the flame a voice saying, "The flame is the symbol of the light. Learn from it, for it is sacred and what it shows forth is the ultimate mystery. Come near, see all by its light but do not touch it, do not profane the shrine, keep violence away from power, keep skill free from cunning, keep reverent and use what is sent you but never think that you fully understand; always be ready to learn and always be ready to welcome those who would come for the shelter and comfort of the flame you guard."

And then you began to doze with a sense of wonder and mystery and safety and security blended and you knew that somehow the home hearth was both the most familiar place in the world and also the most mysterious.

That was the inner reason why the family was not altogether unready when one evening there was a whine outside the door and father rose quietly to open it. He held a staff in his hand but did not strike with it. On the step was a wolf cub. It started back, its

little hackles up and tried to growl but the growl became a whine. It drew away but the cold was cruel and it was evidently starving. It gasped and came up to the step again and then its small legs gave way and the whine became so small a whinny, so like what the youngest round the hearth always made when it wanted aid, that mother rose right up and father stood aside. She came back to the hearth with the wolfling in her hands and told the rest to keep away. But soon they were all round too, and after a little while the cub was on his feet.

"Still, what will happen when he's grown?" was in everyone's mind. But they knew the answer in their hearts, and as the will and the creative power is there, and there lies also that door through which other people come in and hear what we really mean, the cub heard the answer too. It was a very powerful answer. It had to be, for he had a very powerful prejudice against trusting that sort of oddity that now stood above him, towering on its hind legs but really with such feeble little teeth that it had to break up its food with its hands before it could get it down its own throat.

Here was the carnivore come in, and it was among its prey. Time and again that sort of thought would come into its mind but always that sharp icicle was melted by the warm flow of trust that came up from its heart . . . just as the children trusted him, and that made him feel they were his own, he could protect them.

The story was, of course, a long one. But far shorter than any of the parts of the tale we have looked in on, up to now. Generations of fathers and mothers and children came round the hearth and children grew up to be parents and grandparents and slept by the hearth and by the door—and even more quickly ran the generations of the dogs of the house. For now males and females had come into the hearth circle and raised their puppies right in the glow and the fire became such a close friend even to them that when it was too hot, instead of cringing with fear and running off into the night, the young dogs would speak sharply to the flame, growling at it and telling it that it wasn't mannerly to scorch your dog and man guests seated round your altar table. •

And all this was very nice and romantic and sentimental, of course, but still surely, if you were to be a realist, the original mistake made by the branch of our stock that went off and became a carnivorous wolf, that remained! There he was, friendly and domesticated and great fun and really repentant for what he had made himself into. But he was still fatally enchanted and imprisoned in a beast form. The curse stuck. Of course, he had great goodness but wasn't it true that once you had had your wish, however much you changed in character and were really once more a friend at heart, still the form you had wished yourself into, that held!

The Wish That Was Given Away

Then one evening when the year was at the shortest, the frost at its hardest, the fire at its friendliest with bright blades of flame keeping the cold at the door . . . everyone was gathered at the hearth. They had had the fine dinner that you then took to make you ready to wish the sun a very quick and complete and happy recovery from that exhaustion and shortening of his working day which he had been suffering from for the last three or four moons. When it was over, everyone in turn was asked by grandmother to have their wish. Very solemnly they were to tell it to the very heart of the fire, always saying, of course, if it is not for the best, if it is not for everyone's good, give me something better.

At last everyone had had their wishes. They were all proper ones and everyone felt, with a settled warmth round the heart, that they would be granted—and for those which were not, a still better substitute would be found. Indeed, only the very youngest remained to have his. He was half asleep with his arm round the biggest dog's neck and they were grunting some nonsense in each others' ears for they were the closest of friends and seldom went about without each other.

"Wish, son," said the grandmother, putting a very worn index

finger on his still very smooth forehead and he waked up and looked into the fire.

But the first thing he said was, "Look, the winged person is in the fire."

Grandmother said, "Very well, so make your wish equal to his presence."

And the youngest got up supporting his still somewhat chubby legs, which had gone to sleep on their own, by holding on to the big wolf head that looked up to buttress him. "I wish that he were like me, could do all I can do." The hound put up its paw touching the boy on the breast, who now stood sturdily on his legs. "Oh, I do wish it for him."

The animal put up its other paw. The boy took both in his hands. The mastiff swayed and staggered but the child put the paws on his own shoulders and held his friend from falling. They stood like this for a moment. Then the flame under the log whirled up, the dog winced and fell to the floor.

Someone in the group laughed. "Little one, you have lost your wish. Did you want him to walk like a man and have our hands?" and he laughed again.

"Hush, hush," it was grandmother speaking. "Oh, please, be silent. Didn't you understand, don't you see, he's asked for something we none of us had the courage to ask, for none of us loved the dog as much as he." Everyone was silent now and the room was nearly dark for the fire had itself fallen to sleep after that one flash. All they could see now was grandmother's face, for she had bent right down on her knees till the last embers lit her features. They saw her and she had no wrinkles any more and the hair that was white as an old bone by day now was white as the full moon. Her lips moved softly but they could hear, "It will take long and it will take Love, but the speed will depend on the Love. Love will race against Time. Love alone can outrace Time. Quicker than Light he must be and may be. For Love must go back to where Life fell down, raise it up and bear it back, in time. Is it possible? Is it possible? Not only birth but rebirth, not only preservation but redemption, not only a flame kept alive but where the fire had died down, once again the flame rekindled?" A last small blue flame floated above the red ashes and found its reflection in her eyes. But they thought that it was not her voice but one that came as the flame vanished, "Be it unto you according to your faith."

Yes, it was slow. To be as exact as we can be, it took perhaps some eight thousand years—that is, down to today, for the story is not finished yet and no one knows how it will end. Eight thousand years—the whole length of what we call human history. For the Dog has been with us, we now know, from the moment we made the first settlements that you might call something bigger than a single home and rather smaller than a village. Quite early he came to be buried alongside ourselves, showing that we thought he had the same mysterious life as ourselves.[1]

But of course, eight thousand years is just nothing when you're dealing with the magic art of taking flesh and bone and making

them turn into new shapes, grow into new forms. Why, it took
some eleven or twelve million years for the sensitive generalized
squirrel-like person, who was so like what we ourselves were then,
to turn into a wolf. So you see, the way up was much faster
than the way down. You don't generally hear that. It is not thought
to be possible. "Too good to be true," say the people who have
grown so knowing that they know more and more things that can
never happen and can never be done—and you will notice that
such wonderful things never do happen when that sort of clever
person is about. He certainly can make things not happen and so
he denies that other people—not at all like himself—can make
them happen. For the point is—and it is a very sharp one—if
you are good enough to deserve the best things, the best things
do come true. Certainly we have discovered in the case of the
Dog that this wonderful re-gift did take place.

  So again let's try, through Gabriel's eyes, to see the story of
this amazing discovery, more amazing really than all the past
progress. A great husky comes romping in. He's now as fine a dog
as you could wish to see—none of the slinking wolf about him any
more. He's thoroughly at home in the human home just as much
as any of the humans. Everyone is happy—the home is surely a
complete setup. What more does anyone want—what more is
there to want than just more of what you know, and like, and
have, and, if you work hard, can get more of? There are the dogs
and now the horses have come in to the outer ring and can be
ridden and driven to plough. And there is even a henlike body
that likes laying its eggs—quite large ones and quite a lot of them
—in the roof thatch. Further, there's a cow of a sort that likes
being fed and next likes being milked. And even a cattish creature
that you don't drive away because she keeps the mice out of the
garner where you put the wheat. You're surrounded by an ever-
widening belt of ally animals. Surely that's the way to live. For

each of them, in exchange for quite a little keep, gives you more food and more help. You are rich now and knowing, you, the little fellow who waited; you have become so powerful that not only have you become the conqueror of all but you have made a number of your rivals willing and profitable slaves. You begin to think there's nothing more to know than this—how to get richer. That was the general feeling.

But way back before we became rich at all, back before we were really at all what you'd call human, you remember there was always hanging about at the back of our group, someone, or sometimes some two, who asked questions. It wasn't done in any fresh or smart way. Indeed, the questioner was always rather slow in getting in on the goods, always tending to get left behind. But he did keep on tagging along at the tail end. And now he's in the house that has grown to be quite a big place, almost what you'd call one family village. For this little-noticed person is also the small boy who asked as his wish that his dog-friend might become a man.

If you ask questions of that kind and have wishes of that sort, practical people tend to leave you out of the running—out of the rush that goes straight after its nose, after what looks good and smells good. This slow one, therefore, now keeps mostly out of the way. He is left the slower, quieter jobs, such as looking after the fire. When anyone—child or pup—is sick or overtired, he serves as nurse. When the dog has a thorn in its foot Hob-by-the-Fire gets it out.

One day he was doing this more by touch than by sight, as you do if you have real healing hands—and his eyes were looking dreamily at his other charge, the fire. And it suddenly stirred itself from a doze, throwing a gleam of light into his puzzling mind.

"At your old question again, aren't you?" the fire asked.

"Suppose I am," said Hob stirring himself too. He looked from the bright flame to the hound's paw laid trustfully in his two hands. In the dancing light the paw seemed a poor, doubtful, half-blighted bud of a thing, while his two hands looked exactly what the paw should have flowered into. And might still? The further notion flashed into his mind as he glanced back at the flame. The flame nodded.

"Why it's obvious, isn't it?" Hob couldn't say whether it was he or the flame who was actually whispering the thought. It didn't matter; they were thinking it together.

"Why should the dog stay dog?"

"It's wonderful enough, isn't it, that he's ceased to be wolf?"

"Wonderful, yes, but wonderful enough? I wonder?"

"You mean?" "Do you mean, now that his paw is in your hand, that you have really had your wish?" Hob with his fingers felt the blunted tendons and the stub-ended pads that once had been halfway fingers and might have become full ones. He ran his hand up round the pointed cruel-fanged jaw. The dog (the friendly spirit in the wolf-frame) permitted him to push back the black lips and expose the narrow palate set with the flesh-tearing teeth.[2] "You see, it is still a wolf, isn't it?" said the flame that moved, in the great purple mouth of the hearth, like a golden tongue.

"Could it be anything else?"

"Well, you wished that when you were a child, and did I say No?"

"Yes," replied Hob as his mind rose up and went back hunting up its memories, "yes I did, and, ever so long before that, didn't I ask whether I couldn't do something like that for someone who had got stuck up and sealed in with their mistaken wishes?"

"Yes, you asked whether you could give any of them any of your unused wish-power."

"It has begun to work, hasn't it?"

"Yes," said the flame.

"Need it stop?"

"That depends," said the flame and flickered up the chimney.

From that time Hob became even more hobbish. The house, we've seen, was now quite a big rambling place and that helped Hob. For the place had grown to have quite a number of rooms. All kinds of lean-to's, sheds, verandas, porches and forecourts have gathered round the old central room. And there, in the center of that room, is the central thing of all, the center hearth. That fireplace now has become so old and traditional and reverenced that it now has this the oldest, the first room, the place where the fire first became part of the home, all to itself. There are secondary fires, later hearths, that serve in the other places for other special practical uses. All of these may fetch their flame from the central hearth when they need. They may rise and fall. It, the central innermost one, it alone is now the seat of the undying fire. And its room, that first room, now at the very center of the house, has now all its windows blocked by the other rooms that have grown up round it on every side and lean against it. Its only light now comes down from the great central smoke-flue. Its only view is of the smoky sparks going up to the cold stars.

Hob, then, naturally found himself drawn in to be that central fire's watcher. Hero Hal, the horse rider, would come whistling through the outer rooms. The big dogs pricked their ears. And even the one that Hob—Hiero Hob as he was now called—had healed, gave the fire-watcher in the dark central room a lick with his tongue and was gone.

"Will they stay only when they are ill?" sighed Hob. "Are they quite content to remain dogs as long as they can race and hunt with the horses?" His sigh seemed to rouse the hearth flame. It shone out brightly and Hob, out of the corner of his eye, saw that its golden gleam had picked up two small green reflections. He put out his hand. It touched a small head that yet, even in that place of the peace (he could feel), laid back its ears at his caress, hardly daring to trust. But after a half a dozen strokes the little figure, almost crawling, came and curled up on Hob's lap. The flame thought it would have a stretch and yawn. By its light Hob saw a small shrinking animal.

"I think I'll die down again," said the fire. "You see, he's really rather afraid of the light. But you wait, you'll see that your wish is being answered. Here is one that will stay by the hearth, by you, and become your attendant—you the priest, tender of me The Flame, of which this visible flame, you already know, is but my shadow."

And the visible flame sank down for when you arrive what need is there of your shadow, when the sun rises what need of the candle. Hob put his forehead in the ashes, for he knew the dark was now more full of true light than he could bear to look on. And the little doglike creature that loved the night—we call him a Jackal—sheltered himself against Hob. He trembled, but he did not try to run away.

"Will he be the one who shall grow?" asked Hob, "As I wished that he should grow?"

"What do you think?" The voice was so soft that it might be no more than the soft ashes folding over one on another as the fire made them into a coverlet for itself. "Think back. It wouldn't be impossible, would it? After all, it was always from the weakest that the really new power sprang. It was because your lot were ready to stay so long helpless and feeble that you are now all at the top."

So Hob felt that was enough. Anyhow his little Jackal stayed with him and took all the love he needed to show it, till it seemed his very shadow. And people said, "Old Hierophant Hob and his little dog! Do you know, I believe that that little slinking jack that's always with him, is his other self—his animal double. Some of his soul has gone into it." And surely some of the Jackal had got right into Hob's heart. That was the beginning of what is now called—and not understood—Totemism. It's a pity that when you can name and describe a thing then so often the time's past when you could really make it work. Anyhow, Hob and his Totem-jackal were uncannily close. There was no doubt they understood each other well beyond words. When, then, it was Hob's turn to go into the longer sleep—the one we mistakenly call death—and Hob's old garment of a worn-out body was tucked away in the deep dry earth by the holy hearth, the little Jackal crouched on the mound and those who came in and out to ask things of the invisible Flame or to see themselves more clearly in Its Light— they heard the jackal whimpering to itself, or its master. So they called the little night-dog Anubis and when they began to think that death really made you distant and banished you forever— they thought that Anubis knew the way that the dead went and could lead you that path when you had to go. Certain it was that if he went out with you in the dark he could lead you safely home when you couldn't see a thing.

Of course, Hob hadn't gone away. He had simply stepped out of his old clothes and gone to change into another suit. Indeed, quite a number of people knew that, if they happened to be by when the time came for this shifting into new clothes. At that moment they would hear Hiero Hob say in a voice that got softer and softer, "Oh, invisible light, now your visible shadow I can see no longer, for these eyes of flesh are worn out. Give me, there-fore, to see You with my inner eye as You are." And they saw with the clear sense of their minds, in that clear still dark place, that then Hob stepped out of his old stiff robe and lifted off those old, dimmed windshield flesh eyes, and went straight toward the flame that took him to itself. And then, after he had gazed his fill, the flame wove for him another fresh flesh garment which he put on, grew to full size and sat once again for a spell of fire-tending and life-cherishing.

If You Go Back You Can Really Go On

So it was, century by century and millennia by millennia, that Hob came back. So too, on an even more rapid beat, did his little totem-companion keep on returning. Always Hob was taking that small body and those light paws, touching them with a faith that hardly knew what it was daring to ask. For whether Hob knew it or not (at least with his surface mind) his deep wish—more deep and powerful than that which had given the Horse its hoofs, the Tiger its claws—had begun to work.

"There is nothing more wonderful than creation," said Hob to himself. And then asked, "Could there not be one thing more, one thing more wonderful?"

But doubt chilled him, counterquestioning, "Wouldn't that be too good to be true?"

The whisper rose in him, the flame sank down and a cold draft stirred the heavy curtains of the shrine room.

The Smoke which had been rising serenely up to the evening sky, came down a bitter cloud round the hearth. Hob gathered the whimpering Fox to himself to shelter it from the choking fume. As his hands went over its eyes to keep them from the singeing smoke they noticed something his eye hadn't noticed. Surely the forehead of his little familiar was not so low? It was beginning to swell up like a bubble of air left free to rise to the surface. His wonder seemed to clear the air again. Anyhow the flame sprung up once more and Hob hurried to see if his eyes would confirm his touch. They did. He ran his fingers round the slim head. Sure enough, the jaw muscles, as he traced their pull, had begun to loosen up and then out. The little brain that had been confined by the grip of the jaw was being unbound.

"Watch well." The flame was now dancing and signaling as men at a victory kindle beacons to tell the good news. "Now if you will, you may rejoice, for you are seeing something that no living being has ever seen before. This is the miracle that beside which even the miracle of creation is not so wonderful."

"Have you, then, answered me? Have I been given my wish?" Hob cried.

"It is a beginning, is it not?" questioned the flame as it settled down again into the ashes. Hob at that moment was at the end of one of his suits. It was time to shift into another.

"Lord," he said looking at the flame setting in the embers, looking right through it at the Flame invisible, "Now let your servant depart in peace for my eyes have seen Your salvation." And once again he slept by the hearth while a new garment was made for him, and once again he returned in it, to cherish Anubis into new and further freedom. For some of the gains he had won for his dog friend began to endure. Now they were beginning to be written in his flesh and bone from one generation to the next.

The flame, too, was ever new. Whenever it died down it sprang up fresher, brighter. It kept on beckoning Hob forward. "You haven't really yet seen the completion of the salvage, have you?" it asked.

"No, I suppose not," said Hob. "But it's so wonderful that his head can have altered, can there be more? Is it possible?"

"That depends on you," said the flame once again, and with that it dipped and was gone, for that's its exit line always.

Sure enough, that wasn't the end. It wasn't the end because Hob kept on playing with the Jackal's paws and his mind kept on playing with the thought that the poor little fellow ought to have a hand in things, ought to have his hand back. The fact is that the change begun in the bones of the head did begin to flow through the whole body. The forelimbs did begin to alter—to alter back. The little nimble-footed Jackal was never a heavy-weight. But see, as Hob plays with it, the little fellow is losing even his featliness. The Wolf had stretched stiffly out its delicate questing forelimb that it had inherited from the small questing ancestor of us all, had grown it out till it came to be as stiff and specialized as an oar. That was in order to swing it along tirelessly in the track of its exhausted prey.

"But the wolf wasn't that way once, at the start, even, of being a wolf," said the flame, darting up to answer Hob's unspoken question. Hob thought about that.

Then once one day a mother wolf was killed. Hob took the puppies and brought them up. They turned into fine loyal hunters. But that wasn't Hob's business. That was to think and puzzle right to the edge of what we call heart-break but it might just as well be called mind-wake. The small puppies had been so unlike wolves when he had had to feed them with milk. Why couldn't they stay as gently, helplessly free?

"If that is so," said the dark flame suddenly touching the inner-most spot in him where heart and mind meet, "if that is so, why not just trace it back?"

There was a flash of inner light in Hob's mind and he said to the flame, "Then, of course, before they are born, they are even freer and more like us?"

One day another she-wolf was killed, ripped right open and

her young had yet to be born. Hob didn't shrink back, though he didn't like blood and guts. For the Light said, "Look," and sure enough, the little unborn embryos were pudgy-headed, their eyes weren't side-leering things but getting on for being straight-in-front-looking pairs of binoculars and their paws were really something you might take as a promise of becoming hands.

Hob went back to his hearth place. His familiar, the Jackal, crept into his lap. "So you're already imprisoned. Only if you could go back before birth could you be free. You'd have somehow to be so looked after and loved by someone that you wouldn't give up. But something in you—the real deep wish-power—gave up, went back on you, began turning you into a wolfling, before you were born. So the love that could untie you would have to reach you before birth. It's too late. You can't be reborn. I could never give you the hand I want you to have." And he looked down at the small animal and it looked up at him dumbly across the gap they couldn't close. With one hand Hob stroked the Jackal's paw, with the other he fed the fire. The flame rose and stretched itself, as one does after sleep.

"But why stop at birth?" it questioned. "You know you don't stop at death. If love and understanding can go on through Death, is there any reason why they shouldn't go back through Birth? Isn't creation making something quite new? If it can do that in the future, why not with the past? I don't see what Time has to do with it one way or the other." The flame, you see, had become quite garrulous, fluttering and purring to itself.

Hob evidently was listening with all his might, in fact with that kind of will to understand which is really the same as the will to believe and is the final and right form of that will-with-all-your-will which we have seen all through the history of our lot, being used wrong by the animals that went off and out on the side-tracks. Everyone has found who has tried—that if you listen with

all your heart, you can really be told lots you never thought you
or anyone else could know.

The tongue of flame had now, as it did when talkative, become
a glowing tongue moving in the great purple hollow mouth made
by the hearth and its coving. Hob realized that he was actually, as
we say, hanging on the words of a great Announcer who was about
to make a great announcement.

"Summon the others," said Gabriel. "They will be needed. You
can't do this by yourself. This has to be a mass movement. The
commune must meet."

Hob went out and found mother making bread in her great
oven. "I can't come just now," she said, "surely once a week is
time enough to look in on the First and Last Fire? I have to take
care of the means or how shall we live?"

"Man does not live by bread only," said Hob, "but by every
word that comes from the flame of the Innermost," and she got
up and came with him.

He called in at the smithy where the furnace was panting and
the father smith banging with his hammer and the workman said,
"I've all these tools to fix, that plough coulter, these sickles and
scythes against the harvest. Can't leave the job just now."

"Not by might nor by power but by spirit?" Hob asked, and
father Thor flung down his hammer and came along.

Hob went the rounds of the whole big village of a house, a small
town under one roof, and he gathered them all from the oldest
to the youngest. Hero Hal was there. He asked if he might bring
his dogs and Hob answered, "And the horse too." And the woman
who milked the cow brought her friend also.

The central room was much larger than it looked, for it was
hard to see its actual shape, but it was full to the curtained doors
by the time the family with all its totems—which only means
fellow tribesmen—were gathered together.

"I have the honor and the pleasure," said Gabriel's tongue in his finest major domo and toastmaster voice—for of course he is the patron angel of all announcers—"to announce not merely to you mankind but to all of you, my Master's children, good tidings of great joy—deliverance for all who wish to have it for the love of others and for the love of Heaven. For," and he turned specially to the human folk, "if you will, and because your Hob has so desired it, through you shall all the tribes of life be blessed." And now he turned the beam of his attention solely on Hob. Mother Hertha saw first and drew back; then father Thor bent down; Hero Hal squatted down suddenly on his hunkers as the Scotch say, like a little boy with his jaw dropped open in surprise. The animals, though, as the light reached them, actually pushed forward toward it. For, though brighter than any fire they had ever seen, it was warmer, more friendly than any Christmas blaze they had ever felt. This, of course, was to be expected because in point of fact it was just the Light of Life itself, the warmth of a Love that is far braver than the strongest beast in all the world.

For Hob was alight. That was the matter. The little bumbling, stay-by-the-fire and sit-in-the-corner fellow whom everyone liked but everyone felt really was not much use, Hob was now the fire, he was so alight that though it was a joy to look at the brightness you couldn't make out his shape any longer. He had lost every trace of that thing we call personality. But as the flames played round him and seemed to pass in and out of him they thought they heard someone saying, "This is a son in whom I am pleased."

Then Gabriel's voice could be heard again, again as master of ceremonies. He was speaking to the animals who were now determined to get into that bath of glowing life and enjoy themselves. "Order, please, order. First come, first served." The jackal was first in the queue. "Hob, as you are his sponsor, hold him up and wish for him."

Hob held his godchild so that it could stand facing the hearth from which the audible flame was addressing them. The flame bent down to the little jackal-like dog and spoke in quite the intimate tone that a really well-trained cashier uses when you go to his big bank and his official-looking window with your small check, *How will you take it? In what form would you like it?*

The dog raised itself on its hind legs, put out ineffective paws, glanced to and fro at the face that shone at it like a friendly fire but which appeared to the dog (because it couldn't focus its eyes as we say *binocularly*) rather blurry and vague.

But Gabriel could understand its wish. "You desire once again to be able to handle, that is your first wish."

The dog bayed and whined.

"And your second wish is that you should be able to see straight and see things in the round and in perspective."

The dog blinked and tried all it could to focus clearly on the bright questioning, flaming eyes.

"And finally, you desire to be able to think as clearly as you can feel, and understand as you can love."

The dog gave a small short confused yap, but there was no doubt it was an assent. And then it fell back into Hob's lap, for

standing on your hind legs is very tiring and wishing with your deep creative heart is even more so.

But Gabriel was now clearly visible as a great blaze of flame far brighter than any fire the hearth had ever held—in fact he was right in the middle of the fire and making it a combination bonfire and fireworks display—but with no danger to anyone's fur or robes. And now the Archangel became quite judicial or perhaps one should say like the impressive cashier when he says: *I must just see what your balance is.* "You know," Gabriel pointed out in that checking-over voice, "you know you have been overdrawing your account on the bank of life for some eleven million years and there is very little left from the original securities vested by your endowing parent in your name. And you will want a very great deal for your present large scheme of reorganization. Indeed, no one till now has ever thought of making such a venture. It would need an unprecedentedly large amount of liquid assets. No," and his voice was cool and clear as a bell at closing time, "no, you can't really meet it out of your resources. It is quite out of the question, quite."

"But I'm very sorry for my past misspending," said the Jackal. "And what's more I simply can't go on like this being so little use to those I live with and love."

"Did you hear that?" asked the Archangel.

And all round the hearth, human voices said, "We did."

"Will you then advance him a loan?" Gabriel wanted to know.

And as quick as before, the others said, "Done."

They had answered with all the decision of an archangel so that Gabriel smiled at his favorite word being taken out of his mouth. But he clearly thought they had every right to do so. For he turned to the Jackal who was watching him and remarked, "We have now, I think, enough liquid securities for your promotion. As for your using them, it still won't be easy."

"But it will be possible? I shall get free? I shall understand," yapped the beast in the depth of its character.

"Well," said the Archangel, "I've never known it really fail unless the principal party in some way wanted it to fail and lost heart. It will depend on you. Here's what you have to do. You'll have to give up all those things which you thought made you a self-respecting and respected beast. At least (though you're not much of a wolf), at least the rabbits were afraid of you. You'll have to become even more helpless than that. For that is the only way you'll ever go on learning humility and trust—by becoming actually helpless and dependent. You may not have been strong but you have been athletic in your lithe way—are you ready to give that up?"

"I am," said the soul of the Jackal.

"And are you ready to give up your cunning and put yourself in the hands of others and yield all your defenses?"

Again the small beast gulped in its throat, keeping its green eyes on the golden flame figure.

"That means," said the figure, "that you are ready to become like a puppy and stay so—never really grow up and become competent?"

"I will."

"Now hold up your front paw." Hob helping it, the creature put out its front limb stiffly and rigidly, rather like that silly thing the Nazi salute. And the flame bent out toward it and the Jackal whined and winced and as it did so its front paw twisted and shrunk and it was the paw no longer of a hunting wolf-like creature, it was quite different—you can see it on the sacred temple dog, the Pekinese, a little bent pud of a paw on which it waddles like a puppy.

Then the flame leaped out again and again the animal whined, a whine which ended in a kind of snuffle, for its sharp snout had

STORIES OF THE PERSON WHO GAVE AWAY HIS WISH

blunted under the blow of the flame as though it has been putty tapped by a mallet. Father Thor whispered, "That's the way iron becomes soft in the furnace. Can we melt and be rewrought?"

This change in the Jackal's nose, of course, made him snuffle quite a lot. But though this was not so good for his nose it was a great gain for his eyes—for they were now like ours, in line, so that he could see the same object clearly at the same time with both of them. And above them his forehead bulged out till it was really getting like a human forehead.

"There," said the angelic voice to the group of friends who had been crouching round making, for the last few thousand years, the hearth and flame of good will in which the Jackal could be melted back into the primal form. "There, you see, he's a puppy now forever. Now what about trying to go still further back and so come further forward." Then, turning to the temple dog he said, "Would you really wish to go back still further and so recapture more of the original liberty?" And seeing that it assented, he went on. "That means you must go not merely back to puppyhood as you have gone and be content to stay there in dependence on others, it means that you must let be worked in you the last wonderful miracle. Go back into the womb and be born again."

"But it can't happen? Besides, what would be the use? How could he ever live if he did that?" A few whispers rose and the temperature of loving good will and delighted wonder began to drop dangerously.

But Hob had been through that already. He held on to his godchild and kept his eyes on the flame.

And then Gabriel said, "Look." He spread his robe till it was like a great sheet of flame, steady and clear as a golden ground glass screen. And there appeared glimmering on it all the animals that had sprung from the little tree Mouse, all the animals that

had grown into the various species of mammals whose stories
we have been telling in these tales—and lots, myriads more we
couldn't get in. But there was evidently one rule of selection, it
was evidently a show "For Mothers Only." All these animals
were mother animals and they had their young still held within
them. There were Sheep and Deer and Goats and Oxen—Horses
and Giraffes, Rabbits and Bats, Beavers and Hippos, Seals and
Whales—in fact, the whole Noah's ark and some more. Of
course, the Whale, Seal, and some of the others wouldn't need
an ark in a flood. And, as the sheet of flame was glass-like, so in
that field were the animals' bodies also. They processed round, as
you may see colored figures go circling round if you put trans-
parencies on a big glass ball, light it from within and then spin it
slowly. And as each mother beast came into view they saw the
wonder of her life-giving body far, far better than any X rays
could ever show it you. For one thing, whenever, in that magic
lens, the onlookers wanted to see closely any detail, that part of
the picture became so large that they could understand it at a
glance. So they could see, in case after case, animal after animal,
its young growing; blowing up even more wonderfully than a
glassmaker blows an iridescent goblet. And they didn't need
Gabriel to act as lecturer and show them that as the tiny round
ball of life took shape and became what you could see was a
proper animal, each (though its mother might be a wolf or a
rabbit, a bat or a cow) didn't look in the least like what it was
going to be born as later. On the contrary, it looked, would you
believe it, as though it might almost end by being what you have
become. Indeed even more so. For there was quite a good promise
of a roundish, foreheady head. There seemed more than a chance
that these small persons, when they bloomed out of this bud,
would want to go, not on all fours but more or less up-ended and
with their hands well out and open to things. Then what you

suspected came in with a sudden slam of conviction. For as you concentrated and focused to see the hand clearly—of course it was magnified until you could see it larger than your own—from the budding tips of the two forelimbs there fringed out[1] not actual fingers but (there was no doubt of it) faint chalky lines, five of them. No hoof, no talon, no paw showed as yet. No, instead there was the shadow and promise of a true hand—here was the chalk, the lime being poured out, jetted out, so that round these cores, should the wish hold (should not a false wish make the whole fine purpose shrink and miscarry and misform), there might grow the instrument of understanding, the conductor's baton, following which eye and brain and indeed the whole body might advance in an unbelievably beautiful dance of life.

"Oh, I see, I see," it did not need the Archangel to speak, for Hob could now speak for him. "I see, here is the promise and though it has been forsworn, yet it is still there. We could call it out again, if we would, if we cared."

Then Gabriel spoke again, "For millions of years, it is true, the offer has been made and rejected. But still it is renewed, at every prebirth growth. Maybe it is never really withdrawn. But the price of recalling it, when it has sunk so deep and imprisoned itself so completely, goes so far down that some people have said it is as deep as Hell itself. It all depends on the urge, the daring to plumb

as far down as that. If one wishes to, I see no reason why he
should not harrow up even that brick-hard soil and bring again
to the surface and the light the imprisoned seed. Can that which
has once been sown by the Great Sower ever really die? Does it
not wait until someone cares enough to bring it back again rejoic-
ing, bearing his sheaves with him."

Of course, Gabriel wasn't being so stupid as to say this in this
absurd way with those absurd squiggles and sounds we call words.
He said it right in their hearts and he was able to say it because
Hob was listening so hard for them all so that the others just had
to attend. And the Jackal held in Hob's lap—it, too, could not
fail to attend, because Hob was holding it in his mind and heart
just as the mother animal holds the young before birth and gives
it all the blood and flesh that it needs to grow. And because they
were all listening at that level, according to the size of their hearts
and minds (just like the size of a receiving set and aerial permits
the quality of reception you can have), they could all believe, and
as far as they could believe it could happen.

"Remember," Gabriel closed, "remember, it isn't finished, for
it need never finish until you are tired and think you have done
enough—this is just a beginning. In the beginning, the beginning . . ."

The angel drew up the flame with him through the opening by

which the incense smoke rose to the heavens. But even when he was gone from them they could still hear his voice murmuring like the sea, "How inexhaustibly wonderful Thou art. Praise to Thee not merely as Creator but as Redeemer, not merely for what You have made but for what you have restored."

Hob Falls Asleep and the Animals Fall Back

The place had become dark. It was hard to tell the time in that central chamber. You could see changes clearly enough if you were in the other rooms. For instance, that second hearth that had become the forge—it grew until it became so big and efficient, it worked so incessantly and had such a big output, it looked as though it would never need again to get a single spark more of the first fire from the innermost hearth. Even the bakehouse oven became so large and elaborate that plans were made (every five years or so) to run it so well that in the end everyone would have bread and so wouldn't need any longer to ask any questions, seek any advice or offer any appeals. And this wasn't, at the start, the fault of the forge men or the bakehouse workers. It was largely the fault of Hob himself. For Hob was human—in spite of his moments when he was alight with the flame. He was human and that simply means unfinished. No more than the smallest and youngest of us, could he afford to sit down and take time off and feel he had really done enough and knew enough. And sometimes he did relax and quite badly. For you see, in a way his job, though it looked less to do, was, as a matter of fact, harder than anyone else's. Their jobs, as you might say, kept them going. The swing of the hammer keeps your eye on the anvil. The bread in the oven reminds you to keep an eye on the fire—or your nose will be irritated by the smell of burning crust and your mouth and the mouths of others will be even more irritated by getting no bread.

But in that innermost place there was nothing to tell you where you were—you had to keep on reminding yourself. For there, Will-Be is just as real as Now. It is the Hub-Place where everything pivots—the place where anything may happen if you wish with your full will—and nothing happens if you don't. At that central hearth you can be at the place the animals were when they made their magic choices and so became what they are. So, just because that place and its atmosphere is so magical it is all too easy in there to fall into vague fancies, or to spend all your time in thinking about the past and making it live again for you— that's the way a lot of professorial Hobs do spend their lives—or even—and this has been very common with the clerical Hobs— just dozing between one meal and the next.

Indeed, quite a number of times the great face of Gabriel would look down through the wide chimney and observe the hearth, as we look through a telescope at the moon. And he would whisper down the flue, as through a speaking tube, "Hob, wake up! wake up! The cloth that is still aweaving can be unraveled. The pot is still to be baked, one shower of rain and it goes back to mud. Your work of remolding your animal friend is only begun. All you have as yet is a promise. I've shown you what could happen —you must clinch it, actualize it. All that has happened yet is simply a glimpse of what could be. Remember how I showed you, when all of you were starting out on your mammal story, remember how I showed you your glossy fur coats, when you still had nothing really but scales. And when there were only swamps and gum trees, you were let see the golden grain fields that were yet to grow. All I gave you then was hope and a hair, a grass-blade and a blessing. So now, for the love of Heaven rouse yourself. What I've inspired in you, that you must fulfill."

But Hob didn't look up. He was having one of his off days—or indeed we would be more exact to say one of his off lives—sunk in sluggish or fanciful sleep. When he couldn't shake himself out of that for several lives on end, then the center hearth became apparently nothing but a choked heap of ashes. Even if you stoked it there only came out a bitter dust and fume. Then people began to say that there had never really been any fire there—that it was all a superstitious story started by that lazy selfish fraud, Hob. Better clear out the whole frowsty place and make it into a clean bedroom for babies or a henhouse. And soon the whole house began to fail. The forge and the bakehouse, having begun by boasting that they could manage far better on their own, began to fight. The forge became an arsenal—all its skill which should have helped build and repair the house and make the tools for ever better farming, now went into making tools the better to kill people. The bakery was raided and burned. Anarchy and starvation brought the whole place to ruin.

Naturally, then, the animals began to suffer from this abominable setback. The Dog didn't go on. It ceased its struggle to get out of its imprisoning wolf-body. We've seen that it had been helped to come to the state at which it was a permanent puppy. But it just stuck there and became a sour little lap dog, a little cross-grained cuss of a pup. Look at most Pekinese—pop-eyed asthmatics, helpless but arrogant and irritable. Are they proof of progress? They are temple dogs and aren't they perfect illustrations of a wish gone wrong? Looking at them it might seem that this is the result of religion just sunk to be magic. Or perhaps we have made the animals in the form of ourselves—could you have a cleverer dog-picture of a pompous self-important little priest?

And as the Dog stuck still as a pop-eyed Pekinese, another animal stuck still also at the stage it had reached. A second wild beast had begun to follow the Dog (though they didn't like each other in the least and still find that a problem) toward the fire of freedom which would smelt off its crusted animal armor. As we have seen, the Cat had been let hang about the corn-garner. It paid; for, with it about, the Mice kept out of the grain—the

Chicken could usually flop out of its way. But, of all the hangers-on of the house, puss certainly seemed the poorest candidate for civilized company. It was about as safe to touch her as to touch a charged battery. Still she (as did the Jackal) liked dark and quiet and warmth. So for a few thousand years she'd been stealing in and sitting by the darker non-dog side of the hearth, especially when it was kitten-time and kitten-time is really almost half the time for female cats. The Cat learned that by the hearth the kittens were safe and a cat hates having to move house when the nursery is full. Next the kittens, who didn't mind much where they got warmth, would, when they were on their own, stray over

to Hob—they also liked to play, liked his way of teasing them with straws.

Two different streams of Cats came in from the wild spit-and-lash Lynxes and such-like furry fiends. One is the sort we know best and comes up from ancient Egypt. The other is the blue-eyed Siamese. They have become quite tame, in a way, as we know. But the two points which we have to prick into our mind are not encouraging. The first is that, with all our care of their bodies, we have somehow never got close enough to their minds —or should we say their hearts?—so that their bodies would begin to modify, begin to lose their savage flesh-tearing equipment. The Chinese priests, the Mongolian Hobs, succeeded in making their Pekinese temple dogs into permanent puppies. The second point is even more serious. Ever since that time, thousands of years ago (for the Egyptians certainly began taming cats—and lots of other animals besides—not only the Jackal but the Cheetah, the Gazelle and the Rabbit—four or five thousand years ago), we have never succeeded in bringing in from the wild and

taming another of all the wild cats. The clever Greeks even—when they wanted a cat, had to send to Egypt. Is it possible that you can only really tame if you are somehow at home with all life? Is it possible that that at-homeness and harmlessness does not come from being clever and being able to take things to pieces and to think about them detachedly, but from being able to feel with them, to feel one with them?

However that may be, the fact is that we have somehow lost the magic of taming. But that last thin dawn of hope belongs to another story—in the future. It may be that true taming is the lost secret behind the thing called totemism; when you actually felt that in spite of any difference of form, you-and-your-animal-totem were one because you were one life. The wisest of men have been marked not only by the wisdom of the things they have told us—they have been equally well recognized by the reaction of beasts toward them. They have been trusted by the wild animals, they have often been instantaneous tamers.

Well, we have seen the Cat coming in behind the Jackal and starting on the way of becoming tame. The first tame Dog was called Anubis and the cat was called Bes. And everything seemed set for the most interesting experiment in the world's history. But since then the moving picture has stuck. The temple dog hasn't gone on. In Egypt, where he started on the path to rewin freedom, he has gone back. No one now tames jackals and makes them part of God's house. Anubis, once the messenger of God, is now represented in our world only by the wily little wild Fox he once was—when the story of his rewinning, his redemption, began six thousand years ago. In Australia there is another canine. He's called the Dingo and is somewhere between the Fox and the Wolf. He puzzled the biologists till they discovered that he is a true Dog, but one that we let drop and it has fallen back again into wolfdom. With the Pekinese we succeeded in, as it were, patent-

Bes.

ing its freedom for it, by growing the Dog back
into puppy form and making it possible for
that puppy form to be inherited by its children
—but even there that freedom has not been
developed. It remains a half-sprouted seed. As
to the Cat, there we see not even the progress registered in the
Dog—claws are as hopelessly cruel as ever. What fairy tale could
be odder and more puzzling? What has gone wrong with our
magic gift—how have we mislaid it? Have we sold out for the
clever, highly polished, gadget-covered lamp of mechanical science?
Sold the old lamp of a traditional wisdom and instant insight?

There's no doubt we did begin to work a miracle—the miracle
of miracles. For a while we did let flow through us that wonder-
working power whereby you can melt out from a wild animal the
savage form and features which its passions have grown round it
to express themselves. Once we did know how to give back to
dangerous beasts the freedom and trustfulness (for freedom and
trust are two sides of the one thing) which these beasts had lost,
literally millions of years back. While our ancestors were still
living such a simple life that we would call them scarcely civilized—
lacking cars, cinemas, atom bombs and plastic surgery—they seem
to have found the way to untie the hard knot into which the Dog
had tied itself through mistaken wishing. And they had begun to
work quite a bit on the Cat's tangle, too. They did it, evidently;
in not more than sixty generations of our
lives. Their first attempts at it must have
been pretty fumbling.

But surely to transmute a mind is more
fun and more useful than transmuting a
metal. To open up a mind that has shut
itself into a little blind spitfire of reflexes
—until that mind becomes curious, in-

Anubis

terested, affectionate—surely that's the real alchemy? To release the immense creative wish-energy locked up in every creature—surely that's far more worth while than the release of blind, deadly atom energy?

When we look back down our past history and our achieved triumphs as men all the way from the wishing Lizards in the first willing Group—that part of the record is full of hope. But what have we done with this hope and promise? The work has fallen down, we have thrown it aside when we had just begun it. We must go on with it. All the machines we can ever invent, will never get us out of the deepening rut that, with their aid, we have dug for ourselves. All the machinery in the world ends in being nothing but a cruel trap, if we fail to go on with the greatest invention of all—the supreme power, the power which comes straight out from the Creative Inexhaustible Life Himself—the power to give life and freedom, to remold in new creative liberty.

"And then?" One asks that at the end of every story. And one should ask and wonder about that, at the end of this the biggest of all stories. The answer to: "And then?" is "And now." For that means the question is turned around. The story is ended but isn't over. True, we have finished the tale as something that can be told—but at once we go on trying to tell something even more wonderful—a tale which has never been told—because no one knows what the actors in it will do. All we know is that this tale can end, will end, as we wish. We still have our wish-power mainly unspent. We have the answer in ourselves—it's nowhere else. "And then?" The solution is now up to us. The story will end as we choose—as we choose to have the wish to tell it.

NOTES AND APPENDIX

Notes

PROLOGUE

Hair and warm blood seem to have been a double development of the protomammals: the hair being derived from the reptilian scales, the warm blood system from the reptilian cold blood system. The climate appears to have altered simultaneously, more oxygen and less carbon dioxide becoming present. This was unfavorable to the saurians, favorable to the mammals. The mainly resinous trees also tended to disappear and trees more suitable for mammalian diet (resin is not) grew instead.

The Sea-Loungers

1. The upper vertebrae of whales are all fused.

2. Some fifteen years ago it was discovered that the deep sounding whales possess an adaptation whereby on coming up from great pressures the nitrogen does not bubble in the blood and so "caisson disease" does not take place in them. For a long while physiologists refused to accept the sounding records obtained by whalers because it was pointed out that any ordinary mammal being brought up from such a depth would undoubtedly suffer this serious disability.

3. The great blue whale of the Antarctic still seems to have a continuous meatus probably because it does not dive deep save for avoiding pursuit by man, its main food being now on the surface. But the sperm whale which dives for its cuttlefish prey has grown over and blocked the ear passage (see "Hearing in Cetacea" by Robert Clarke, *Nature*, June 19, 1948, p. 980).

4. The giant blue whale of the Antarctic (Report of 1946-47 British Scientific Expedition of Antarctic whaling ground) when 90 feet long

weighs 120 tons, 40 per cent of his body is muscle, he generates 520 horsepower and can for ten minutes sprint at twenty knots while he cruises between fourteen and fifteen.

5. Herman Melville says a harpoon thrown by a strong man will bounce off a whale's forehead.

6. Frank Bullen, F.Z.S., the sea naturalist, notes this inability of the whales to tolerate changes of sea temperature for long.

7. The Orca or killer whale has become so fierce that it attacks even more furiously than the shark. One was found with the still undigested remains of thirteen porpoises and seals in its stomach and it had been choked to death by the skin of the last seal which it was attempting to swallow in too large fragments.

The Mowing-Machines

1. Henry Fairfield Osborn in the American Museum of Natural History, New York, has shown the evolution of the horse from an almost harelike little fellow of five toes up and up with a steady loss of toes to the giant one-toed hopelessly specialized horse of today.

The Blood-Lusters

1. All the carnivores, even dogs, if protein intake is lowered, get convulsions.

2. Dissection shows that whereas in the human body the thyroid—the gland of sustained effort—is large and the suprarenals—the glands of conflict—small: in the carnivores—such as the tigers—the thyroid is small, the suprarenals large.

3. The seal and the dugong and manatee seem to be an example of retrogressive convergence. The seal appears to be derived from an unguiculate; the dugong and manatee from an ungulate stock. The seal is a carnivore; the dugong and manatee, herbivorous.

4. It has been found in forest wild life reserves that if the large carnivores are killed off the large herbivores do not benefit. On the contrary, they suffer from bacterial and virus epidemics. Many, too, become so sluggish that they will browse kneeling down until the knee joint begins to be diseased.

The Air-Walkers

1. Dr. Hartridge of London has shown that the bat's larynx produces no less than four kinds of sound: (1) A buzz which seems used to keep them in touch with their fellows—the human ear can just hear this if close to the animal. (2) Their echo-sounding note· at

seven thousand cycles a second—with this they can fly blind. If the ears are covered or if near a surface which yields a very poor echo they collide—hence sometimes getting caught in hair. The "call" is sent out every quarter of a second. (3) A call that rises to thirty to seventy thousand cycles a second. (4) A click. Several of these sounds can be produced simultaneously. They probably have three vibrating structures in the larynx.

2. Pteranodon, one of the flying lizards, had wings twenty feet across. The span is so great that the pectoral arch is fixed to the vertebrae like a pelvis.

The Dancing Danglers

1. Dr. W. E. LeGros Clark, F.R.S., Head of Department of Human Anatomy, Oxford, communication to Linnean Society April 22, 1948, summarizing "African Fossil Primates discovered during 1947." "The finds suggest that the adoption of the brachiating habits (moving about by swinging by their arms from tree to tree) which are characteristic of the modern apes, may have been a relatively late acquisition." And, "It is probable indeed, that Proconsul (the name given to a species of fossil ape much less specialized and less ape-like than any ape today: its bones are now being found by Dr. Leakey in Kenya) was not a brachiating specialist but led a more cursorial type of existence." Because its thigh bone seems to have been "long, slender and straight." The humerus (the upper arm bone) "is also of somewhat delicate construction and lacks the powerful muscular ridges associated with brachiating habits."

2. See Drs. W. N. and L. Kellogg, *Ape and Child*. The child chimpanzee was always oversetting objects it tried to pick up because its fingers were too long.

3. See Sir Grafton Elliot-Smith, F.R.S., on conjoint development of brain and hand.

The Dangling Drowsers

1. The true sloths are now of two sorts—the two- and three-toed species. They have both developed a peculiar hair which is devised so that it houses algae—one sort of this hair having longitudinal cracks, the other lateral—the algae in the damp tropics grow sufficiently to give the hair the greenish look of old moss. They have "a reptilian tenacity of life surviving heavy injuries and large doses of poisons." Their main danger is from the harpy eagle.

The Pig Who Chose Punch

1. The series of species that runs up to the mammoth and the elephant seems to have risen from a tapir-sized creature with an ordinary muzzle (Moeritherium), Paleomastodon (two tusks in lower, two and snoutlike muzzle in upper jaw), Tetrabelodon (equipped likewise), mastodon—lower jaw still with short tusks: Stegodon: Mammoth. There was off the main line the Dinotherium who had rake tusks hooking down and in, from the lower jaw. This was evidently a poor invention. The mastodons could still bend their necks and long snouts so as to touch earth. Elephas Antiquus was considerably bigger than either the present Indian or African elephants.

2. The mammoth's coat as we know, from the extremely good drawings of our stone and ice age ancestors and from actual frozen mammoth found a number of times in Siberia, was of two thicknesses like the present muskox, a fur mat underneath and over that long, coarse dark hair that almost reached the ground. "The mammoth belongs to the most highly specialized section of the group elephas furthest from the mastodon." (Richard Lydekker, FRS. FGS. FZS.)

3. The upper vertebrae are fused and the back of the skull flattened (as in the elephants) so as to give muscle purchase to carry the huge tusks.

The Tusks That Took Over

1. The African elephant has a trunk with two flaps—or fingertips—to the nostril. A single tusk of an African elephant has been found weighing 226½ pounds, and bigger are known. The present-day elephant skull is full of cavities to make it light. As these develop during its growth they seem to show they are an adaptation to the evolution of the big head and huge, heavy tusks. So for the same reason the neck is short and inflexible. The elephant has no gall bladder, the liver is small and simple. "To support the trunk and ponderous tusks the head must be of proportionate size. The brain does not increase much during growth. An extraordinary development of air cells, therefore, takes place in nearly all the bones of the cranium. Their development, scarcely commenced in the newborn animal, gradually enlarges as the growth of the creature proceeds." (Richard Lydekker).

The Small Sore One

1. Naked, blind and toothless at birth, the young shrews soon run about snapping at everything within their reach. The shrew secretes

an odor in the armpit which is like rancid cheese and makes it secure against attacks of all its enemies save the owl. The eyes are nearly concealed by fur. Excessively voracious and pugnacious, if two meet they fight and the conquered is eaten.

The One Who Thought the Way Was Underground

1. The mole is almost as voracious and fierce as the shrew mouse. The eyes now only register light and dark. The ear too, only just appears through the skin and is invisible under the fur having no conch. If two meet, one is killed and eaten. The genus extends over a great part of the globe.

The Fool Who Put Horns on His Nose

1. The Asian rhinoceros still attacks with a tusk somewhat similar to a boar's.
2. The horn of the rhinoceros is made of adapted columnar cells similar to hair. It is not bone at all nor connected with the skull but sprouts like hair from the skin of the nose.

The Cat That Was Caught by the Claws in Its Mouth

1. Machaerodus, the sabre-toothed tiger, has very short feet, only four toes on hind pair. The fangs grew until they extended along grooves each side of lower jaw and hung down well below.
2. A marsupial machaerodus was found in the thirties of this century and in the Argentine (described by an Argentine zoologist).

He Who Got His Finger Stuck in the Pie

1. The Aye-Aye, "the most remarkable and aberrant of all the Madagascar Lemurs." The third finger is almost twice as long as any of the others and proportionately thin, the penlike nail at the end impaling wood-boring grubs at the end of their burrows.

The So-Heavy-Weight That He Gave Up Standing

1. One of the strangest facts found out lately about our human evolution up from subman levels is that it was not the brain that led; it followed. The brain follows the long bones—the bones that set us up upright—and, most strange, the long bones follow the teeth. Our teeth were decisive. They took the lead in holding on to smallness and neatness and keeping in scale and proportion. Our teeth became (or maybe hung on to being) human before our bodies became so, and even longer before our brains became manful. It looks as though if our teeth hadn't shown this commendable restraint we'd never have had any brains worth talking about for, for one thing, we'd

never have talked. See also the embryological evidence of the retardation of the teeth in early foetal life. Sir Arthur Keith's studies in human anatomy.

2. Dr. Robert Broom's remarkable discoveries in South Africa of (possibly Pliocene) fossils of the ape man Plesianthropos (the near-to man) have yielded, up to date, remains sufficient to show that (1) his elbow, though freer than the apes' we know, was not as free as ours. Probably he couldn't stretch his arms full straight. (2) His hand bones show that his hands were not being used as forepaws to get him over the ground or sling him through the trees. But still they were not so shaped as to give him our widely responsive grasp of things. (3) As to his foot, his ankle bones would show that he had ankles that could hold him straight up, while his pelvis (which of course has to act as a kind of ankle to the spine) evidently held his spine fairly vertical too. And finally (4) the hole where the spinal cord goes into the skull (the *foramen magnum*) and the bosses low down on the skull where it meets the neck and where the neck muscles root (in the condyles) both show that his spine held his head fairly upright. But still, right down where the ascent begins, his big toe still shows a certain indecisiveness. And the decision has not been taken for good, as to whether the big toe is to be content to make its whole business the task of bearing the weight of holding up the body and the head and setting free the hands, or whether it will itself play at picking up things on its own.

3. The name tree-mouse has here been used, instead of tree-shrew. The tree-shrew of Celebes, the Tupoia, which does not seem to be at all a shrewish creature, is, of all surviving creatures, supposed to represent most closely the mammals' common ancestor.

4. One of the two surviving species of gorilla lives in the Congo Mountains where great beds of wild celery grow. It is still strictly vegetarian. Gorillas have been found with an arm span of thirteen feet. The writer was told by an explorer that he knew of a case in which a gorilla with one pull tore off a Negro porter's arm at the shoulder. They have been also known to kill by thrusting their stub-thumb into their provoker's body. They attack the full-grown Negroes because these shoot them. But they do not attack the pygmies because the pygmies consider the gorilla their totem-brother. Hence, in the Belgian Congo, whites who wished to study gorillas were ordered to take pygmies with them as porters, with whom the whites would be safe. The gorilla is easily frightened. At the Berlin Zoo a full-grown

specimen suddenly felled his keeper, but, on the man's screaming, the ape rushed away, cowering in a corner and the keeper made his escape.

Since the above was written the late Dr. Broom had discovered the fossil thumb bone of one of these hominids. It appears to be almost as "opposable" as that of modern man. However, largely due to these finds in Africa, and now the latest find on the Caspian, a new, complex and completely counter theory has arisen. This is the theory of Professor Frederick Wood Jones in his authoritative essay, *The Hallmarks of Mankind*. The whole of this thesis is so brilliant, profound and radical that it has to be considered more fully in the Appendix to this book's Preface.

5. According to the Roman astrologer Nigidius Figulus the scales were invented by a certain Mochos. A black-figure Cyrenaic vase has the words "*Silpho Machos*, weigher of the Silphion herb" written above the figure of a king's clerk weighing bales of Silphion herb. Coptic *Mache* is an old Egyptian word (*maha*(t)) for "Balance." The Greeks called a lever *mochlos*, "the little beam."

6. "The angel Michael holding the balance of judgment, weighing the souls, is originally nothing but the 'God of the Balance' Macha-el (Abatur with the Scales, of the Mandeans) vocalized by pious Jewish popular etymology Mi-Ka-'el, 'who was like unto God.' " Robert Eisler, *The Royal Art of Astrology*, p. 101.

7. In the Mahayana (Buddhist) Scriptures the following recipe is given for those who desire the gift of invisibility: "For two years manage to abstain from ever once thinking of yourself: then you will find that no one will notice you."

The One Who Stood Up for Good
1. For the very early association of man with the fruit trees—perhaps a preglacial and almost symbiotic relationship—see Mr. H. B. Stevens' remarkable and suggestive book, *The Recovery of Culture*.

The Finding of the Friend in the Fire
1. The tapetum glow was seen in Kamela's (the wolf child) eyes as long as she still followed the nocturnal lupine life. As soon as she became a human day-liver, night-sleeper, this gleam disappeared. (See *The Wolf Child*, by Zing and Singh, Harper & Brothers.)

The Wish That Was Given Away
1. The second Pumpelly expedition to Anu near the Caspian found dogs buried with the humans.

2. See "The Dog, the Foetalization of the Wolf," by the head of the Hamburg School of Animal Psychology. *Antiquity* (London), 1932.

If You Go Back You Can Really Go On

1. X-ray photographs of the lamb in the womb of the ewe have shown five traces of calcium lines extending from the forefeet buds at very early stages of the embryo life.

Appendix

All explanations and theories as to whence man came, how long he has been in coming and what forces drove him upward have excited passions the temperatures of which have mounted to theological intensities. Naturally enough. For much is at stake—our fundamental notion as to man's nature. Few books hâd more influence on this generation than H. G. Wells' *Outline of History.* Sidney Webb (Lord Passfield) told the present writer that in two years it sold in greater numbers than any other book had ever sold. The author began by establishing his hero's character. Man, he said, is sprung from a singularly fierce ape. That statement has been increasingly questioned by evidence which has accumulated rapidly since the *Outline* was written. And lately the evidence has reached a point that compels us to revise our whole outlook.

To glance first at the whole field of evolution: There have now been held six views as to how species arise and evolve. First was Buffon's (died 1788). He held changes in environment cause changes in physique. Next came Lamark's (in 1809) *Philosophie Zoologique.* Changes of environment change the habits of animals and so the animals' changed habits change their physique. The third was the Darwin-Russell theory of Natural Selection (Darwin's *Origin of Species,* 1859): Living forms tending to vary, some of these variations are inherited. As all forms breed in excess of resources, few survive. Those who do are, obviously, varieties more successful in the struggle and so their dependents are those who inherit the earth. The fourth view was advanced by Samuel Butler (*Life and Habit,* 1877): A race memory accompanies the physical reproductive germ, and habits acquired by one generation do in the end become instincts. The fifth view was advanced by De Vries, when (1900) Abbe Mendel's work (first published in 1865) was recovered. Species are not continuously connected. A new species is a sudden appearance. Random mutations by separate genes cause new species. Natural Selection is, at best, secondary. The fifth view brings us to the latest decade. All the genes act together to make a common gene environment within the animal. Natural Selection tends to work between these gene complexes. Further, Professor R. A. Fisher—to whom this fifth view owes so much—was said (when the President of the Royal Society presented him with the Darwin Medal) to have established the view that this form of Natural Selection may mitigate the bad and enhance the good effects of hereditary units. Hence there is a power "not ourselves" but in us, making for progress. The sixth view has been called Organic Selection. The gene combinations best suited to the habits of the whole creature could prevail against those gene combinations which fail to help those habits. Something like this view was advanced fifty years ago but (as with Mendel's work) has returned for consideration today as an explanation of preferences of habitat. Changes in behavior can bring about selection of different gene complexes. As Professor A. C. Hardy, F.R.S., has said, Samuel Butler's idea of subconscious racial memory, but on a group and not an individual basis, may best account for our present findings.

These general considerations—suggesting that the life-process need not always be regarded as a blind confusion—indicate that we must reconsider our view of mankind. The popular view of man is still based on some assumptions that have become too questionable. Most people still think that as our stock has only of late (perhaps not more than a few hundred thousand years) derived from one of the large ape species, he would naturally still inherit the gloominess of the gorilla, the surliness of the orang or the violent temper of the chimpanzee. Students of the subject were of course aware that the discovery of the Swanscombe skull had shown that there was clear evidence that modern (neoanthropic) man was far older than had been allowed. Since then a number of lines of research have proved fruitful. (1) The present apes have been found to be decadent forms of far less specialized types (see Dr. Leakey's work referred to above) and it would seem that as the famous Eoanthropos skull is so late that it was not prior to neoanthropic man, so probably all the ape-men which Dr.

Broom and Professor Dart have discovered in South Africa, are—as mentioned above—ancestral (less specialized) forms of the present apes and not of present men. (2) Dr. H. V. Vallois in *Comptes Rendu* of the Paris Academy of Sciences (Feb., 1949) has described a human skull (found at Fontéchevade, Charante) which though dated by implements as Tayacian and by animal remains as of the "warm" fauna of the pre-Wurm Glaciation, is nevertheless in no wise Neanderthal. And now, (May 21, 1951) Dr. Comb of the University of Pennsylvania reports from an undisturbed limestone cave above the southern Caspian shore that in the lowest levels he has discovered the remains of three human beings. The dating cannot be less than seventy-five thousand years and may well be one hundred thousand. Skull and long bones are of a modern type of man. (3) The Abbe Teilhard de Chardin, than whom there are few paleontologists more authoritative, has issued a thesis to show that biological evolution is purposive and its goal, not its accident, is consciousness and free-will. (4) But most important of all has been Professor Frederick Wood Jones' publication (under the title, *Hallmarks of Mankind*) of the substance of his Linacre and Arris and Gaul Lectures. Therein, from anatomical evidence (from the mature skeleton and from that of the embryo) and from fossil evidence he establishes the following supremely important points: that man, because he has retained unspecialized primitive mammal characteristics is immensely old. Man is not ascended from the ape; the apes are descended from, are degenerate forms of a "manling," a tarsier type that could walk upright. Man is not the "foetalization of the ape" but the retention and enlargement of some tarsoid form. He has specialized in unspecialization, and so we may say, as Dr. Hugh Miller of the University of California has put it, man is yet to become a species, i.e., confined in a special form. Man therefore is man, the master of all beasts and not only the crown but the promise of all life, because he has retained sensitiveness, the upright carriage and the open, exploratory, tentative, unspecialized hand.

Further, Dr. Jones shows that mammalian evolution, the Tertiary stocks, are full of parallelism and convergence: e.g. (1) As Smith Woodward established, the horse type, the hypertrophied one-toed quadruped runner, arose more than once from a generalized form. (2) The lemur stock did give rise to a creature (Nesopithecus) which had characteristics of the New World monkey (Cebus) but it became extinct and the lemurs are not the ancestors of any present monkey or ape. (3) The monkey type has twice arisen. (4) But the apes are not descendants of the monkeys. There is then a tendency in more than one species to a parallel degeneracy. And likewise, at several points in the evolution of not yet fully specialized stocks, there is a convergency to pro-generate, to give rise to an advanced stock, advanced in the retentive development of generalized capacity, e.g., in the steady extension of the brain, "the largest mass of un-specialized tissue in the body." In this work of Dr. Jones, which is the summation of research papers issued since 1918, there is then presented by an authority an ordered sequence of evidence which it is hard for an open mind to reject. In this thesis alone—leaving aside the wealth of further research, which is added to now nearly every month—there is to be found argued conclusively, with convincing detail of anatomical, embryological and paleontological proof, the main thesis which gives the theme to these symbolic fairy tales.